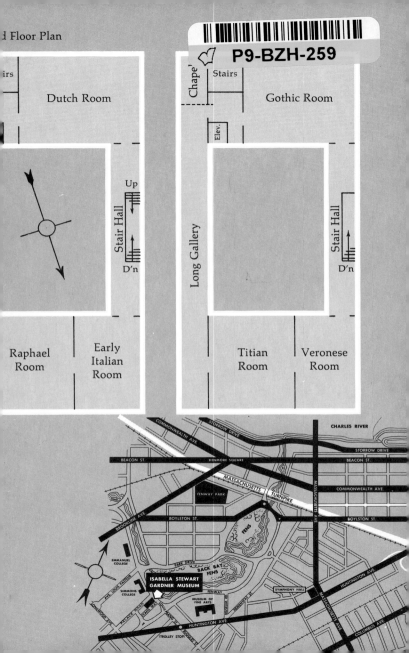

GUIDE

THE COURT

GUIDE

TO THE COLLECTION

ISABELLA STEWART GARDNER MUSEUM

PUBLISHED BY THE TRUSTEES

BOSTON, MASSACHUSETTS 02115

CONTENTS

	3	Note to the Reader
	6	Mrs. Gardner: A Biographical Sketch
FIRST	13	Yellow Room
FLOOR	15	Blue Room
I	16	Spanish Chapel
	17	Spanish Cloister
	18	Chinese Loggia
	20	Court
	23	East Cloister
	24	North Cloister
	24	Macknight Room
	25	West Cloister
SECOND	29	Stair Hall, North
FLOOR	29	Early Italian Room
II	36	Raphael Room
	42	Short Gallery
	47	Little Salon
	49	Tapestry Room
	53	Second Floor Passage
	54	Dutch Room
	63	Stair Hall, South
THIRD	64	Stair Hall, North
FLOOR	65	Veronese Room
III	72	Titian Room
	79	Long Gallery
	90	Chapel
	93	Third Floor Passage
	93	Gothic Room
	102	Stair Hall, South
	105	Index of the Artists

© 1976 Isabella Stewart Gardner Museum
Library of Congress Catalog Card Number: 76-4176
Second Edition, March 1976; revised, 1980
ISBN 0-914660-02-0

NOTE TO THE READER

This *Guide* is prepared for visitors who wish to locate the more important objects in the Isabella Stewart Gardner Museum. The collection contains a large number of works which are familiar to serious students of art and the subjects of countless published discussions. Other objects have been included because they reflect the taste of Mrs. Gardner and offer that variety which refreshes the eye and the spirit. Certainly no absolute standard for judging art need be considered here. Visitors are invited to study and enjoy the collection according to their own interests and fancies.

Whenever possible the name of the artist is given but this is at times surprisingly difficult to determine. Often there is no signature; sometimes there may be grounds for doubting the validity of a signature. The identity of some artists will probably always be unknown; in other cases the artist is identified by an accepted inscription or by clear documentation. Between the known and the unknown there is a limbo well populated with works the origin of which, in date, artist, and place, is warmly debated. The results of these controversies may effect changes in prestige and market value, but they can have no effect on the intrinsic quality of the objects themselves.

An object attributed to the "studio of" a known artist is by one who probably was a close associate. A less personal and direct relationship, but one close in time, is indicated with "influenced by"; while "style of" covers those further removed in time. "After" refers to a work by an unknown artist after a known and definitely attributed original.

In this second edition of the *Guide,* the selection of objects for consideration and the revised attributions have depended on the museum's recent publications: *Drawings, Isabella Stewart Gardner Museum* (1968), edited by Rollin van N. Hadley; *European and American Paintings in the Isabella Stewart Gardner Museum* (1974), by Philip Hendy (the first painting catalogue was published in 1931); *Oriental and Islamic Art in the Isabella Stewart Gardner Museum* (1975), by Yasuko Horioka, Marylin Rhie, and Walter Denny; and *Sculpture in the Isabella Stewart Gardner Museum* (to be published in 1976), by Cornelius Vermeule, Walter Cahn, and Rollin van N. Hadley.

It is quite likely that some visitors will take greatest pleasure from the whole appearance of the museum, the relation of the works of art to their setting and to the color and fragrance of the flowering Court. Together, these make up Mrs. Gardner's composition, an embodiment of the concept of a grand house where people might have lived for generations surrounded by things that they cherished.

Her predilection was for the Italian Renaissance, and her vision of a museum was a Venetian palace of the XVc, with galleries open on a courtyard in bloom. The dream became reality, planned in complete detail by Mrs. Gardner, and erected under her constant and sometimes whimsical supervision. Before the architectural drawings were finished she had already decided where each imported pillar, doorway, arch, stone carving, or other structural member would be placed. The building was finished in 1902. It had already been incorporated as a museum in 1900. Upon her death in 1924 Mrs. Gardner's will provided for the maintenance of Fenway Court permanently in its original arrangement.

This arrangement, however, affords the visitor little help in locating the objects considered most important. Often they are not given a conspicuous position and they are placed with little relation to their historical or geographical origins. The result is a set of rooms that have a personal, informal character.

In its principal holdings the catalogued collection consists of approximately 290 paintings, 280 pieces of sculpture, 60 drawings and 130 prints, 460 pieces of furniture, 250 textiles, 240 objects of ceramic and glass, and 350 objects of other kinds, without an enumeration of manuscripts and rare books or of architectural elements set into the building.

MRS. GARDNER: A BIOGRAPHICAL SKETCH

Isabella Stewart Gardner was born in New York City on 14 April 1840, the child of David Stewart, who could trace his ancestry to the XIIc Scottish house of that name, and of Adelia Smith, descendant of Richard Smith, an Englishman who had settled in Boston in 1650. Mrs. Gardner's first connection with Boston came through a visit to Paris, where a friendship with her schoolmate Julia led five years later to marriage with Julia's elder brother, John Lowell Gardner, in 1860. The young couple established themselves in Boston, where her independence of manner and thought excited a good deal of comment.

> She was a fascinating, frail, delicate little creature, delightful to everybody, but determined to lead her life in her own way. Because she was not well, she often spent her morning in bed; this was 'not being done' in Boston, and seemed very peculiar. She discouraged informal, early morning 'running in'; all her life she allowed her friends to take no more liberty than she chose to give; yet she was warm-hearted and always delighted in giving others pleasure. She was considered shy, and during her early married life her health prevented her from going much in society; she was glad to escape frequently to New York and to stay with her parents until her eager husband came to fetch her . . . As soon as she entered the room, interest centered in her: young and old succumbed to her fascination; though she was not beautiful, she produced the effect of beauty; her neck and shoulders were snow-white, her complexion peaches and cream, her eyes a wonderful blue, and her hair golden.

(Morris Carter in *Isabella Stewart Gardner and Fenway Court,* Boston, Published by the Trustees, 3rd ed., 1972, pp. 23-25.)

The birth of her son in 1863 proved to be a fearful ordeal. She lavished great warmth and attention on the boy. When he died two years later, she was crushed. During the two years which followed the boy's death she endured depression and illness. At a doctor's suggestion Mr. Gardner took his wife to Europe, her condition so poor that she had to be carried aboard ship on a mattress. Within a few months, however, she returned home in health and in good spirits.

> Quickly she became one of the most conspicuous members of Boston society. Effervescent, exuberant, reckless, witty, she did whatever she pleased, and the men, the gayest and most brilliant of them, she captivated. . . . It was Mrs. Gardner's rule to select and acquire the best. If she were attending a polo game, she would be escorted to her seat by the best player of the day; the best tenor of the opera, the best painter, the best art critic, the best judge of horses — these, each for a special purpose, were her friends. One of the best business men in town was her husband; and naturally the best dancer in society was pretty regularly her cotillion partner. . . . Such victories the ladies could not forgive. They wrapped themselves in virtue and would have nothing more to do with such an outrageous woman. . . . [Nevertheless] as one man put it, 'every one who has ever talked with her declares that she is the most brilliant, charming, and attractive woman on earth.' (Morris Carter, pp. 29-33.)

In 1874 Mr. and Mrs. Gardner went abroad again, and afterwards with increasing frequency. In a small way she had begun to acquire minor works of art, without thought of forming a collection; but in 1885, in Venice, she began to feel the power of the great masters of the Italian Renaissance. It took time to bring her to decision; it was not until 1888, in Seville, that she bought her first old master, a Madonna by Francisco de Zurbarán (now catalogued as from his studio). It hangs in the Spanish Chapel, on the ground floor. At an irregular but accelerating pace, especially after she received her father's inheritance in 1891, she deliberately became a collector of fine art.

A friendship which was to prove significant had already begun. Like many fashionable Bostonians, Mrs. Gardner had been attending some of the lectures of famous Harvard teachers, and it was perhaps in Professor Charles Eliot Norton's art history class that she met the charming and brilliant young man, Bernard Berenson. He made a strong impression on her, and after his graduation in 1887 she was one of those who helped him go abroad. Devoting himself to the study of Italian art and the correction of attributions, he soon became recognized as a leading connoisseur. From 1894 onwards Mrs. Gardner relied heavily on his advice and assistance in the acquisition of important works of art.

Two traits in Mrs. Gardner which help to reveal her character were her love of music and her perceptive and amiable patronage of talent of every sort. Conductors, composers, players, singers, painters, sculptors, writers, and scholars were all the beneficiaries of her wealth of spirit and money. In a variety of quiet but effective ways she furthered many careers.

At the end of December 1898, Mr. Gardner died, leaving her in full control of his fortune. His death

seemed to have shocked her into an awareness that she, at 58, was no longer young, and she began furiously to work toward the realization of the museum that she and her husband had planned. A few weeks after the funeral she bought land in the recently filled Fens, and while the foundation piles for Fenway Court were being driven left for Europe to look for columns, capitals, arches, ironwork, fireplaces, staircases, and fountains among other architectural elements, which she wished to incorporate into the building. At the same time she continued to add to her collection of masterpieces.

She returned home in December 1899, to supervise construction. The plan was often modified without a moment's notice, and every detail was required to have her specific approval.

The seal which Mrs. Gardner designed for her museum was characteristic: a shield bearing a phoenix, symbol of immortality, and the frank motto, *C'est mon plaisir* (it is my pleasure). It was part of her pleasure to keep her plans for the museum wholly to herself. Neither the architect nor the contractor was permitted to give any explanation or hint, and the Italian workmen, imported especially for the project, could not speak English. The effect, of course, was to whet public curiosity.

By Christmas of 1901 the building was essentially finished, some of the sculpture was in place, and plants were growing in the Court. The first formal event in the new building was an Anglican midnight mass in the Chapel, on Christmas Eve, attended only by six members of the family. Almost equally few and select were the other guests admitted to Fenway Court during the year which followed, while pictures were being hung and furniture arranged. The climax came on New Year's Night 1903, the official opening. Her guests listened to a concert of Bach, Mozart, Chausson, and Schumann played by fifty members of the Boston Symphony Orchestra under Wilhelm Gericke, in a two-story concert hall the upper half of which is now the Tapestry Room. Then the Court doors were opened, and the guests were admitted to a spectacle that was strange indeed in midwinter Boston — the balconies were hung with flame-colored lanterns, numberless candles flickered beyond the archways and windows, there were fragrance and color from the masses of flowering plants, and faint music came from the splashing fountains.

The first public opening was a few weeks later, on 23 February 1903, and from then on Fenway Court was periodically opened to the public, on a limited schedule and with an admittance fee. Mrs. Gardner lived in her great house quietly, giving only an occasional large party, but she enjoyed entertaining the distinguished friends she had acquired over the years, and she continued to buy works of art.

Shortly after Christmas 1919, she suffered a stroke, and thereafter never again walked. Answering a letter from her old friend Count Hans Coudenhove in 1922 (she was then 82) she wrote:

> . . . I haven't a horse or anything now, but I am trying to keep up my courage. I'm quite an invalid, but cheerful to the last degree. I think my mind is all right and I live on it. I keep up a lot of thinking, and am really very much alive. I live in one house, everything else having been sold. This house is very nice, very comfortable, and rather jolly. It is on the outskirts of Boston, not in the country. I have filled it with pictures and works of art, really good things I think, and if there *are* any clever people I see them. I really lead an interesting life. I have music, and both young and old friends. The appropriately old are too old — they seem to have given up the world. Not so I, and I even shove some of the young ones rather close. (Morris Carter, p. 251.)

She died a year and a half later, on 17 July 1924, and was buried in Mount Auburn Cemetery, Cambridge, in the Gardner tomb, between her husband and her son. Her true memorial is this museum.

MATISSE: THE TERRACE, ST. TROPEZ

I

Off the Public Entrance Lobby, to the left, the
YELLOW ROOM

In two bronze cases on the west wall and one by the north wall: letters, sketches, programs, signed photographs and manuscript scores of various musicians, many of whom were friends of Mrs. Gardner's. There are letters from Busoni, Wilhelm Gericke, Percy Grainger, Nellie Melba, Karl Muck, Pierre Monteux and Anna Pavlowa; photographs of Massanet, Paderewski and Johann Strauss; manuscripts by Fauré, Gounod, Anton Rubinstein, C. M. Loeffler and a fragment of a Tchaikovsky score; as well as autographs of Beethoven, Berlioz, Brahms, Liszt, Mendelssohn, Saint Saëns, Richard Strauss and Wagner.

Above the middle case: *Charles Martin Loeffler* (1903), by John Singer Sargent (American, 1856-1925), painted at Fenway Court and given to Mrs. Gardner on her birthday. Loeffler and Franz Kneisel shared the first violin desk of the Boston Symphony Orchestra from 1885 to 1903.

Right: *Love's Greeting*, by Dante Gabriel Rossetti (British, 1828-1882). The theme of lovers in a rose garden was inspired by the French medieval poem, "Roman de la Rose," popular with the Pre-Raphaelite painters.

On the wall opposite, center: *Mme Gaujelin* (1867), by Hilaire Germain Edgar Degas (French, 1834-1917). The sitter, a ballet dancer and actress, is said to have refused this work although she had commissioned it.

To the left: *Nocturne, Blue and Silver: Battersea Reach*, by James A. McNeill Whistler (American, 1834-1903). The view is of London across the Thames.

To the right: an earlier painting by Whistler, *Harmony in Blue and Silver: Trouville*, with the figure of the painter Courbet in the foreground.

DEGAS
MME GAUJELIN

To the right of the stone arched window, high on the wall: *The Terrace, St. Tropez* (1904), by Henri Matisse (French, 1869-1954), depicting the artist's wife at the house of the painter Paul Signac. The gift of Thomas Whittemore (whose portrait by Sargent is in the Macknight Room), this was the first canvas by Matisse to enter an American museum.

In the case: *Viola d'amore,* by Tomaso Eberle (Neapolitan, XVIIIc), given to Mrs. Gardner on her birthday by Loeffler.

Above: *The Roman Tower, Andernach,* by J. M. W. Turner (British, 1775-1851), painted probably in 1817 on a tour of the Rhineland.

In the cabinet, top shelf: hexagonal-shaped porcelain *Bowl* (Chinese, mark and reign of Yüng-cheng, 1723-1735), painted in *famille rose* enamel and decorated with the attributes of the Eight Taoist Immortals. Two *Rice Bowls* with the same provenance are on the second shelf, along with a large *Bowl* (Persian, XIXc), in imitation of late Ming blue-and-white ware.

ON ALL SHELVES: 18 Sèvres plates, with blue dots on a gold ground and borders of flower-wreaths. They bear the mark of the painter Yvernel and the date mark for 1769.

ACROSS THE PUBLIC ENTRANCE LOBBY, THE
BLUE ROOM

The four cases contain letters to Mrs. Gardner from friends who were authors, critics and connoisseurs including Henry Adams, Bernard Berenson, T. S. Eliot, Oliver Wendell Holmes, Julia Ward Howe, Henry James, Matthew Stewart Prichard and George Santayana.

The pictures are of the XIX and early XXc, many of them by artists who were friends or acquaintances of Mrs. Gardner's. Among these are four by John La Farge (American, 1835-1910), two by Antonio Mancini (Italian, 1852-1930), and three by Anders Zorn (Swedish, 1860-1920). Portraits of Mr. and Mrs. Gardner by Mancini and Zorn, respectively, are in the Short Gallery. John Singer Sargent is represented by four oil paintings and seven watercolors. The works by the French painters Corot (1796-1875), Courbet (1819-1877), and Delacroix (1798-1863) were acquired before 1882.

ON THE WALL TO THE LEFT OF THE DOOR FROM THE ENTRANCE LOBBY: *Madame Auguste Manet,* the painter's mother, by Edouard Manet (French, 1832-1883), painted *ca.* 1863 and sold by a grandson of Mme Manet in 1909.

BELOW: *Chez Tortoni,* a sketch, by the same artist, of a patron of a Parisian café, painted several years later than

MANET
CHEZ TORTONI

the portrait above. The name of the man is unknown. The café was one at which Manet habitually took lunch.

ON THE OPPOSITE WALL, TO THE RIGHT OF THE WINDOW: *Henry James,* by his nephew William James (American, 1882-1961). The sitter was a close friend of Mrs. Gardner's, and 100 letters from him are in the museum archives. The portrait was painted in Cambridge and given to Mrs. Gardner in March 1911.

RETURNING THROUGH THE ENTRANCE LOBBY, TO THE LEFT, THE SPANISH CHAPEL

ON THE FLOOR UNDER THE WINDOW: marble *Tomb Relief of a Knight in Armor,* believed to represent a member of the Maldonado family of Salamanca (Spanish, *ca.* 1500).

SET INTO THE WINDOW: several *Painted Glass Panels and Medallions.* The center roundel is of *S. Martin and the Beggar* (French, XVIc). The lower left one shows *S. Benedict Lying in the Briars* (German, XVIc), one of a series designed by Dürer.

TO THE LEFT: painted wood figure of a *Standing Bishop* (Netherlandish or German, XVc).

OPPOSITE THE ALTAR: marble relief of *Two Crowned Female Saints,* the one with a lamb is S. Agnes. The marble itself was once part of a IIIc Roman sarcophagus, but the carving is XIVc Neapolitan.

OVER THE ALTAR: *The Virgin of Mercy,* from the studio of Francisco de Zurbarán (Spanish, 1598-1664), *ca.* 1630-1635. It may have come from the Monastery of the Mercéd Calzada at Seville since the badge of that order is shown at the throat of the Madonna. The canvas was trimmed before 1888, the date of purchase.

The textile of the *Altar Frontal* is XVIc Spanish drawnwork, of hard-twisted heavy linen thread; a band of Italian

needlepoint lace trimming the *Superfrontal* is XVIc reti-
cella work.

Adjoining the Spanish Chapel, the
SPANISH CLOISTER

On the upper level, on either side of the doorway: two
limestone reliefs, the *Entry into Jerusalem* and *Two Kings*
or *Elders of the Apocalypse*. These French Romanesque
figures from the mid-XIIc are from the church of Notre-
Dame-de-la-Couldre at Parthenay, in Poitou.

The wrought iron *Grills, Gates,* and *Railings,* in the
Cloisters, Spanish Chapel, and in the Stairhalls are
Italian and Spanish, XVI-XIXc.

On the east and west walls: *Tiles* (Mexican, XVIIc),
taken from a ruined church in Atlixco, Puebla. They were
bought by the painter Dodge Macknight for Mrs. Gardner and she arranged them in their present pattern.

On the east side: two marble *Sarcophagi* (Roman, IIIc).

On the west side: marble *Sarcophagus* (Roman, in the
style of V or VIc, possibly modern construction).

Limestone *Portal* (French, late XIIc), once the entrance to
a private house in La Réole, near Bordeaux.

The second window beyond: elaborately carved stone
Window Arch (French?, late XVc).

In the alcove: *El Jaleo* (the name of an Andalusian dance)
by John Singer Sargent. Only 26 when he painted it in
1882, he was working in Paris and this was shown in the
Salon of that year. It was based on drawings that he had
made in Spain in 1879. The picture was later acquired by
The Hon. T. Jefferson Coolidge of Boston who gave it to
Mrs. Gardner in 1914 when she had this part of the building altered to provide the present setting. In 1919 Sargent
gave her several of his preliminary sketches.

SARGENT: EL JALEO

FRAMING THE ALCOVE: Moorish *Arch,* designed for this setting, supported by late medieval Italian *Columns with Animal Bases.*

AROUND THE MIRROR AT THE LEFT: five pieces of Egyptian *Woodcarving* (XIII-XIVc). The *Inscription Panels* once decorated the home of a pious Muslim; their message is similar to the sentiment of "home sweet home" samplers.
ON THE WINDOW LEDGE TO THE RIGHT: Turkish *Tile* (Iznik, XVIc), part of a wall-revetment. The medallions of brightly colored tulips, carnations, and hyacinths combine with swaying grape vines and leaves against a flawless white ground.

HIGH ABOVE THE WINDOW: Persian luster *Tile* from a *Mihrab* or Prayer Niche (Kashan, XIIIc). The *thüluth* letters, from a verse of the Koran, are of cobalt blue glaze.

ON THE EAST SIDE ARE STEPS TO THE
CHINESE LOGGIA

TURNING TO THE LEFT: three rectangular *Cinerary Urns.* The one made of sandstone is probably Italian, XVc; the two marble are Roman, imperial period.

AT THE END: stone *Madonna and Child* (French, in the style of the early XIVc). BELOW: Corinthian *Capital* (Roman, IIIc). ABOVE THE MADONNA: stone tablet *Patrician Family at Prayer* (Westphalian, *ca.* 1600). FLANKING THE MADONNA: two marble columns with Hispano-Moresque *Capitals* (Xc or later).

IN A WINDOW AT THE RIGHT : *Stained Glass Panel*, made of fragments from the windows of Rheims Cathedral (XIIIc).

WINDOW SILL, LEFT TO RIGHT: *Woman in the Costume of the Theater* (Roman, IIIc); *Herm of Dionysos* (Graeco-Roman, Archaistic version of a work of the Vc B.C.); *Eros Apoxyomenos* or *Funerary Statue of a Boy* (Graeco-Roman, IIIc); *Torso of a Silvanus* or a *Youthful Male Season* (Graeco-Roman, II or IIIc); *Funerary Statue of a Boy* (Roman, perhaps of the Antonine period); *Torso and Right Leg of Dionysos or Apollo* (Graeco-Roman, *ca.* 50 B.C.); *Bowl with Griffin Heads* (Roman, Ic).

OPPOSITE THE STEPS: door to the Monks' Garden (open to visitors in favorable weather) flanked by *Head of a Roman* and *Veiled Head of a Roman Woman* (Roman, Ic B.C.-A.D. Ic), the former set on a Renaissance garden herm, the latter on a Graeco-Roman garden herm.

TO THE RIGHT, ON THE SILLS OF THE WINDOWS: rectangular *Cinerary Urn* (Roman, 117-138); *Torso of Dionysos* (Graeco-Roman, 140-190); circular *Cinerarium* (Roman, 60-90); rectangular *Cinerary Urn* (Roman, late Julio-Claudian or early Flavian period); and *Torso of a Man* (Graeco-Roman, copy of a work of *ca.* 440 B.C., or earlier).

IN THE BAY WINDOW: bronze *Temple Bell* (Japanese, XIXc).

IN THE PASSAGEWAY BEYOND ARE THE SALES DESK, CAFÉ AND WASH ROOMS.

ON THE OTHER SIDE ON A PEDESTAL: carved limestone *Votive Stele* (Chinese, Eastern Wei dynasty, dated 543 A.D.). It depicts in high relief on the front a Buddha with his hands

CHINESE STELE

in the positions symbolic of "absence of fear" and of "charity." At his left and right appear two monks and two Bodhisattvas; at each edge, in low relief, is a standing figure of Kuan-shih-yin. On the base is a votive inscription with the names of the 78 donors of the stele, and the date of dedication. On the back, in low relief, are two Buddhas preaching to six kneeling monks, flanked by two large Bodhisattvas. The stele is evidently related to the form of Buddhism known as Mahayana (northern) which prevailed in China and Japan.

Across the Spanish Cloister again, through the Portal, into the East Cloister, and to the
COURT

Protected by its roof of glass four stories above, the Court is in bloom throughout the year with plants and flowers supplied by the museum's greenhouses. There are displays of freesia, jasmine and azaleas in the spring, lilies and cineraria at Easter, chrysanthemums in the autumn and poinsettias at Christmas. Many varieties of orchids are shown throughout the year.

The stone arches, columns, capitals, and inset reliefs are partly old, with examples from the Roman, Byzantine, Romanesque, Gothic, and Renaissance periods, and partly modern. In the spandrels of the Cloister arches, and in the panels above the arched windows of the upper floors, are thirty-eight circular stone medallions, carved in relief with animals and birds. These are Venetian and were employed in the embellishment of the façades of buildings from the XIIc onward. The window frames, balconies and balustrades are also from Venetian buildings, but from the XIV-XVIc.

MIDDLE OF THE COURT: *Mosaic Pavement* (Roman, IIc). The head of Medusa is in the center. The mosaic comes from the bathing establishment of a villa near that of Livia's at Primaporta, a few miles north of Rome.

LEFT OF THE PAVEMENT (SOUTH): granite *Horus Hawk* (Egyptian, probably Ptolemaic, 331-300 B.C.). In the Egyptian pantheon the hawk was the sun god Horus, personified on earth by the ruling king.

AT THE BASE OF THE SOUTH WALL: The fountain with its frieze-like *Rim* made up of panels carved with sea animals, monsters, and mythical beings (Venetian, XVIIc) has above it a marble *Relief of a Maenad or Hora* (Graeco-Roman, I or IIc). One of a series of eight dancing maidens, which together formed a small, circular tomb or part of a colossal cylindrical base for a Dionysiac tripod. The two Istrian stone *Dolphins* are Venetian, XVIIc, or later.

ON THE SOUTH WALL, AT THE SECOND STORY: two stone reliefs, (center left) *Peacocks* (Venetian, XIIIc); (center right) *Winged Ox*, with an open book inscribed: *S. Lucas* (Venetian, XIIc); and (far left and right) two *Lion Antefixes* (Tuscan, XIIc).

BEYOND THE PAVEMENT (WEST SIDE): Graeco-Roman marble *Amazon or Artemis the Huntress*, a copy of a Greek original of the late V or early IVc B.C. IN THE NORTHWEST CORNER: headless marble figure of a *Woman in Doric Dress*

GRAECO-ROMAN
PEPLOPHORUS

(Peplophorus), a Graeco-Roman copy of a Greek bronze of *ca.* 455-450 B.C. Acquired by Mrs. Gardner in 1901, the year it was unearthed in Rome near the ancient Gardens of Sallust.

TO THE RIGHT OF THE PAVEMENT (NORTH SIDE): small limestone *Garland Sarcophagus* (Greek imperial, *ca.* 250), with a portrait bust of a child.

IN THE NORTHEAST CORNER: marble *Goddess (Persephone?) or Woman* (Greek, Ic B.C. or A.D., after a work of *ca.* 350 B.C.).

IN FRONT OF THE PAVEMENT (EAST SIDE): marble *Throne* (Roman, Ic), with a bearded, winged figure clothed in Near Eastern garb.

SET INTO THE EAST WALL OF THE COURT; FIRST STORY SPANDRELS: two stone *Saints in Niches* (Venetian, XVc), representing S. John the Baptist and a bishop saint.

Turning back to the
EAST CLOISTER

At the south end: *Fountain*, assembled by Mrs. Gardner
from odd pieces of Italian stone carving. The *Sarcophagus*
with strigilar carving is Roman III or IVc; the *Animal
Bases* are probably late Medieval.

Along the Cloister wall: four stone *Windows* (probably
South Italian, XIV-XVc).
The stone *Doorway* (Central Italian) is inscribed: AVE
MARIA GRATIA PLENA and dated M · D · XII [·]
IVLVS · DXX. The latter refers to Julius II, pope from
1503-1513.

Between the two windows to the left of the doorway:
architectural and sculptural *Fragments from an Ambo* or
large pulpit and reading desk in the church of S. Lucia in
Gaeta (South Italian, XIIIc). Of these, four marble *Reliefs*
framed in a colored mosaic of Cosmati work represent the
winged lion of S. Mark (upper left), the winged bull of S.
Luke (upper right), and (below) a stag and a basilisk.

At the north end, above the archway: large stone *Escutcheon* (Spanish, XVIc). The arms are those which the
Holy Roman Emperor Charles V (1500-1558) adopted
after his marriage to Isabella of Portugal.

To the left, the
NORTH CLOISTER

Carved limestone *Retable* from Lorraine, *ca.* 1425, representing six scenes of the Passion, with the Crucifixion in
the center. The kneeling donors of this work are at each
end, with their patron saints John the Baptist and Catherine of Alexandria. Below: three limestone *Capitals* or
Impost Blocks (French Romanesque, XIIc), depicting, from
left to right, several scenes of the Passion, a calendrical
illustration for March, and perhaps Daniel in the lions'
den. Above: silver *Sanctuary Lamp* (Spanish, XVIIc).

Left, on an inverted capital: marble *Holy Water Basin*
(North Italian, Milan? *ca.* 1100), carved in low relief.

On the Court side, on a column: Istrian stone figure of
S. Christopher (North Italian, XVIc). To the right, on a
capital: *Head of Apollo?*, Graeco-Roman, in the manner
of Praxiteles.

Farther along, flanking the center arch: two marble
Columns with Lion Bases. On the left, a kneeling atlante
shares the burden of support (North Italian, XII or early
XIIIc). On the right, a man, imprisoned in the claws of a
lion, plunges a knife into its flank (Tuscan, XIIc).
The pair of figured *Capitals* are Roman IIIc. From the
complex foliage emerge centaurs with amphorae. Dionysiac figures appear on each side of each capital. The design
is quite rare.

Through the door, the
MACKNIGHT ROOM

This was Mrs. Gardner's favorite sitting-room during her
later years. Ten water colors by Dodge Macknight (American, 1860-1950) predominate, but among the other American artists represented are Louis Kronberg (1872-1965),
Martin Mower (1870-1960), Denman W. Ross (1853-
1935), John H. Twachtman (1853-1902), and Arthur Pope
(1880-1974), one of the original trustees appointed by
Mrs. Gardner.

SARGENT
MRS. GARDNER IN WHITE

ON THE BOOKCASE, RIGHT: bronze bust of *Maria de Acosta Sargent* by Anna Coleman Ladd (American, 1878-1939).

ON THE WALL BEHIND, three pictures by John Singer Sargent. LEFT: *Mrs. Gardner in White.* The watercolor was painted 14 September 1922 at Fenway Court, two years before her death. CENTER: *Rio di San Salvatore*, one of two views of Venice in the room. (The other, *S. Maria dei Gesuati,* is to the right of the mirror.) RIGHT: sketch of *Thomas Whittemore* (1922), the American archaeologist who restored the Byzantine mosaics of Hagia Sophia in 1931.

ACROSS THE ROOM, WEST WALL: bronze *Diana*, by Paul Manship (American, 1885-1966).

LEAVING THE MACKNIGHT ROOM, TO THE RIGHT, THE
WEST CLOISTER

ON THE NORTH WALL: limestone *Tabernacle* (*ca.* 1450), ascribed to Bartolomeo Giolfino (Veronese, *ca.* 1410-1486). Christ as the Man of Sorrows is in the center between SS. John the Baptist and Julian (?). On the pinnacles are the half-figures of the Annunciation with God the Father

ROMAN SARCOPHAGUS

in the middle. The decorative Gothic elements are freely interpreted here, and combine well with the early Renaissance shells which crown the niches.

DIAGONALLY ACROSS: marble statue representing the *Personification of Faith* (Neapolitan, XIVc), standing on a blue stone *Spiral Shaft* (Tuscan, XIII-XIVc).

TO THE RIGHT: marble *Sarcophagus with Satyrs and Maenads Gathering Grapes* (Roman, Severan period, 222-235), probably representing a scene from the life of Dionysos. The lid may have had one or more figures of the deceased reclining on it, as if on an elaborate couch, or was decorated with another Dionysian scene in relief. The elegant carving and balanced composition mark this as one of the finest surviving examples of Roman imperial sarcophagi.

ALONG THE OUTER WALL, RIGHT TO LEFT: four frescoes transferred to linen. *S. Francis* and *The Madonna and Child Enthroned* (Venetian, *ca.* 1400-1450) once formed part of the decoration of a church in the Veneto. *An Angel Catching the Blood of the Redeemer* and *Mater Dolorosa* (Lombard, 1425-1475), fragments from a Crucifixion scene, now lost.

ON COLUMNS (Venetian, XIIc): a stone heraldic *Lion* and a *Female Head* from balustrades or stair rails (both Venetian, XVc).

TO THE LEFT: stone relief of the *Madonna and Child* with the arms of the Venier family of Venice (XVc). BELOW: Roman *Sarcophagus* (*ca.* 125) with strigilar carving and a nameplate in the shape of a Maltese cross.

UNDER THE STAIRS: Venetian *Fountain* (probably XVc) with various small Graeco-Roman and Renaissance heads and torsi.

UNDER THE STAIR LANDING: *Fragment of a Tombstone* (Persian, *ca.* 1475-1490). The intricate carving reflects the calligraphic court style of the capital of Herat at Timurid. The remains of an inscription give part of the epitaph of a prince or holy man. ON THE FLOOR: small stone *Lion* (Venetian, XIVc).

AT THE SOUTH END: Istrian stone *Madonna della Ruota della Carità*, 1522, by Giovanni Maria Mosca (Venetian, active 1515-1553), with the arms of Paolo da Mônte, a manufacturer of rock crystal who commissioned the work. The relief was made for the façade of a building belonging to the Scuola della Carità in Venice.

> THROUGH THE DOORWAY ARE THE OFFICES AND THE PASSAGEWAY TO THE SALES DESK AND WASH ROOM
> Of special note — IN THE PASSAGEWAY: *Kuan-yin* (Chinese, Chin dynasty, first half of the XIIc), painted and gilt wood statue representing the Bodhisattva in the attitude of royal ease.

STAIRWAY TO SECOND FLOOR: the *Stairs* of Istrian stone and the marble *Balustrade* (Venetian, XIXc) are copied from a stairway in the former Fondaco dei Turchi, Venice.

SET INTO THE WALL: two large marble *Slabs* (Venetian, IX-Xc), perhaps from the parapet of a choir. Also, six stone *Cornice Moldings* (Venetian, XI-XIIc), the fragments arranged to form a lintel.

ABOVE: pair of *Gate Doors* from a temple or shrine, with finely-carved panels, and two sets of *Sliding Doors*, painted on natural cedar, depicting *Plovers* and *A Drinking Tiger and Two Fu Dogs* (all Japanese, XVIIIc). AT THE HEAD OF THE STAIRS: painted wood *Panel* in the shape of an open fan, by Kano Yasukuni (1717-1792), showing the legendary Princess Hsi Wang Mu with her attendants.

II

SECOND FLOOR STAIR HALL, NORTH

ALONG THE STAIRWELL: iron *Grill* in two parts, from a bed (Italian, XVIIc).

IN THE CENTER: two large *Columns* of pink Carrara marble (Italian, XVc).

HIGH ON THE LEFT WALL: tapestry, *Noah Builds the Ark*, woven by Van Brugghen (Brussels, mid-XVIIc). This is one of a series of three in the collection, giving the story of Noah.

OPPOSITE: tapestry, *Winter* (Flemish, probably XVIIIc).

BELOW: small carved walnut *Credence* or cupboard (Italian, style of XVIc).

The *Tile Floors* throughout the museum were made for Mrs. Gardner by Henry Mercer of Doylestown, Pa., after XIVc tiles at the Castle Acre Priory, Norfolk, England.

THROUGH THE DOORWAY, THE EARLY ITALIAN ROOM

Although small objects in the room are from other parts of the world, and the furniture is of different periods, the paintings are all Italian and cover a period from about 1320 to 1540.

HIGH ON THE SOUTH (RIGHT) WALL: *The Annunciation*, by an unknown Florentine painter, *ca.* 1365-1395.

BELOW, RIGHT: *Sacra Conversazione*, by Andrea Mantegna (Mantuan, 1430/1-1506), painted late in the artist's career for a nobleman of Mantua. This is perhaps the first Italian picture to follow the Netherlandish custom of seating the Madonna and Child in an open landscape in imaginary conversation with a group of saints.

MANTEGNA
SACRA CONVERSAZIONE

CENTER: small panel painting, *A Prayer Before a Tomb,* by Antonio Cicognara (Ferrarese, active 1480-1500).

LEFT: *The Circumcision,* panel painting by Cosimo Tura (Ferrarese, *ca.* 1430-1495), which includes the figures of S. Joseph holding a taper, Simeon the High Priest, and the prophetess Anna. It may have once been part of the predella for the Roverella altarpiece in S. Giorgio, Ferrara. This and the two panels in the room by Lorenzetti and Giovanni di Paolo have companion panels at the Fogg Art Museum, Cambridge.

BELOW: *The Dormition of the Virgin, with a Nun,* from the studio of Giovanni da Rovezzano (Florentine, *ca.* 1412-1459). It shows Christ among the apostles, taking up the Virgin's soul in the form of a child and the kneeling nun is apparently the donor. This was probably the predella of the altarpiece from S. Giovanni Evangelista in Pratovecchio.

TO THE LEFT, ON THE EAST WALL: *A Young Man in a Scarlet Turban,* tempera on panel, by Masaccio (Florentine, 1401-1428/9), painted probably between 1425 and 1427. One of the first of modern portraits, it expresses the growing hold of secular life on the arts.

The four tall iron *Torchères* along the east wall are Spanish, XIV-XVc.

HIGH ON THE WALL: *Hercules,* fresco by Piero della Francesca (died 1492), an Umbrian who was trained in Florence and then carried Florentine ideas to other parts of Italy. It exemplifies the revival of interest in the human body and Greek mythology. Painted about 1465-1470, it came from the painter's house in Borgo Sansepolcro.

BELOW: the long panel, and its companion panel to the left of the doorway, are by Pesellino (Florentine, 1422-1457). This is *The Triumphs of Fame, Time and Eternity;* the other is *The Triumphs of Love, Chastity and Death.* They illustrate a poetic moral allegory by Petrarch. The theme is demonstrated by the six principal figures, beginning with the panel beyond the door: Love is defeated by Chastity, Chastity by Death, Death by Fame, Fame by Time, and Time is triumphed over by Eternity. At the extreme right of the second panel God and the angels preside in Eternity over a new earth. The panels probably came from the fronts of two wedding coffers, made for the marriage of Piero de' Medici (father of Lorenzo the Magnificent) to Lucrezia Tornabuoni, about 1448. A chest of this type and period is in the Raphael Room.

PIERO DELLA FRANCESCA
HERCULES

SIMONE MARTINI: MADONNA AND CHILD, WITH FOUR SAINTS

ON EITHER SIDE OF THE DOORWAY, RIGHT: *A Lady with a Nosegay*, by Bacchiacca (Florentine, 1494/5-1557).
LEFT: *A Boy in a Scarlet Cap*, by Lorenzo di Credi (Florentine, *ca.* 1448-1537).

ABOVE THE FAR PESELLINO PANEL: polyptych, *The Madonna and Child, with Four Saints* (SS. Paul, Lucy, Catherine, and John the Baptist), by Simone Martini (Sienese, *ca.* 1283-1344). His earliest known work is at Siena and he was employed intermittently by the commune as painter, architect and surveyor. His last years were spent at the papal court in Avignon, where he was befriended by Petrarch. This altarpiece comes from S. Francesco, Orvieto and was painted *ca.* 1320. The figures show Simone's interest in an ideal beauty of form and movement with the emphasis on line and color.

BELOW: walnut *Table* (Italian, XVIIc). ON THE TABLE: *A Turkish Artist*, attributed to Gentile Bellini (Venetian, died 1507), done in pen and gouache on parchment probably in 1479-1480 at the court of Sultan Mohammed II. The costume is that of a courtier. The inscription, upper right, is an Arabic identification of the painter as famous among the Franks.

GENTILE BELLINI
A TURKISH ARTIST

To the left: *A Bishop Saint*, by Michele Giambono (Venetian, active 1420-1462). The panel is part of a now dismembered altarpiece, perhaps originally painted for a church in Padua.

On the north wall, right of the window, above:
The Madonna and Child Before a Rose Hedge, in the style of the early XVc, by a follower of Gentile da Fabriano. The frame may be original.

Below: *The Crucifixion*, by a XVc Umbrian known only as Il Maestro Esiguo (The Tiny Master).

Between the windows, on an easel: triangular tempera panel, *S. Elizabeth of Hungary*, by Ambrogio Lorenzetti (Sienese, active 1319-1347). He died with half the inhabitants of Siena in the great outbreak of the Black Death in 1348. This evidently is one of the upper panels of a large altarpiece.

On the wall behind: *S. Anthony Abbot, with Four Angels*, by Niccolò di Pietro Gerini (Florentine, active 1368-1416). Among the finest of his panels, the composition is solid but formal and dry in the manner of those who followed Giotto without understanding or conveying his spirit.

TO THE LEFT, ON AN EASEL: *The Madonna Enthroned, with Saints and Angels,* by Bartolommeo Bulgarini (Sienese, active 1337-1378).

LEFT OF THE WINDOW, ABOVE: altarpiece with predella, *The Madonna and Child; The Crucifixion,* by an unknown Venetian, second half of the XIVc. BELOW: triptych, tempera on wood, *The Crucifixion, with Saints,* attributed to Paolo di Giovanni Fei (Sienese, active 1369-1411). In the upper parts of the wings is an Annunciation. In the lower parts, left, are SS. Stephen and Anthony Abbot, and right, SS. Catherine and John the Baptist. Such miniature folding altarpieces were fashionable in the XIVc and were produced in greatest number at Siena.

WEST WALL, RIGHT OF THE WINDOW, ABOVE: *The Madonna and Child, SS. Matthew and Francis,* by Bicci di Lorenzo (Florentine, 1373-1472). BELOW: triptych, *The Madonna of Humility, with Saints,* by an unknown Venetian artist of the late XIV to early XVc.

LEFT OF THE WINDOW, ABOVE: *The Dormition and Assumption of the Virgin,* painted before 1434 by Fra Angelico of Fiesole (1400-1455). In the lower part of the picture Christ stands in the center of his disciples, holding the Virgin's soul in the form of a child, while S. Peter sings the 114th psalm. This is in the Byzantine manner of com-

FRA ANGELICO: DORMITION AND ASSUMPTION OF THE VIRGIN (detail)

PISANELLO: SIGISMONDO PANDOLFO MALATESTA

memorating the Virgin's death, a manner gradually super-
seded during the Middle Ages and the Renaissance by the
Assumption, in which Christ receives the Virgin into
Heaven, as depicted in the upper scene. This picture is
one of four reliquary tabernacles made for S. Maria No-
vella, Florence.

BELOW: *The Madonna and Child,* by Pintoricchio (Umbrian, *ca.* 1454-1513).

RIGHT OF THE FIREPLACE: *The Madonna and Child with a
Goldfinch,* by Bernardo Daddi (Florentine, died 1348).

IN THE CASE BELOW: various pieces of metalwork, including
four *Medals* made between 1441-1446. The three by
Pisanello (Italian, died 1450) are of Filippo Maria Visconti,
Duke of Milan; Sigismondo Pandolfo Malatesta, Duke of
Rimini; and Niccolò Piccinino of Perugia. The one by
Matteo de' Pasti (Italian, died 1467) is of Isotta degli Atti,
fourth wife of Sigismondo Malatesta.

LEFT OF THE FIREPLACE: *The Child Jesus Disputing in the
Temple,* by Giovanni di Paolo (Sienese, died 1482/3). This
may be part of a predella of a large altarpiece.

IN THE GLASS CABINET, ON THE TOP SHELF: alabaster *Canopic
Jar* (Egyptian, New Kingdom or later, 1570-1085 B.C.) and
bronze statuette of *Harpocrates* (Egyptian, probably Ptolemaic or Graeco-Roman). SECOND SHELF: Persian luster
Plate with a Scene of Two Lovers (Kashan, *ca.* 1210).

CHINESE HAN BEAR

THIRD SHELF: two bronze *Bears* (Chinese, early Han period, *ca.* Ic), once either part of a tomb treasure or worshiped as cult objects.

IN THE WINDOW: *The Madonna of Humility, with a Donor,* in the style of Gentile da Fabriano (Umbrian, XVc).

IN FRONT OF THE FIREPLACE: pair of high-back *Benches* (Italian, XIXc).

THROUGH THE DOOR IN THE EAST WALL, THE
RAPHAEL ROOM

RIGHT (TOWARDS THE COURT): *A Woman in Green and Crimson,* by Piero del Pollaiuolo (Florentine, *ca.* 1443-1496). The simple costume of the sitter presumes that she was a member of the artist's immediate circle. BELOW: painted *Panel* from an Italian cassone, second half of the XVc, suggesting the influence of Persian silks.

ABOVE, CENTER: *The Annunciation,* attributed to Antoniazzo Romano (Central Italian, active 1452-1512). It has also been ascribed to Melozzo da Forlì, Fiorenzo di Lorenzo and Pier Matteo da Amelia. It decorated the outside wall of the chapel of S. Francis in S. Maria degli Angeli, below Assisi. Painted about 1480 the traditional scene takes place in a XVc Florentine palazzo carefully rendered in the recently developed technique of linear perspective. The three small paintings on the flat of the predella are contemporary, though apparently by another hand. They represent *S. Peter, Christ Rising from the Tomb,* and *S. Paul.*

In front: the Venetian *Settee* (XVIIIc) combines styles of both Louis XV and XVI. On the wall behind: *Embroidery* panel (probably XVIIc Spanish) with the double-headed eagle and crown of the Hapsburg family at the top center.

To the left: *The Madonna and Child,* regarded as a contemporary copy of a painting by Cima da Conegliano (Venetian, died *ca.* 1518).

Below: *A Story from Antiquity,* by Giovanni Maria Falconetti (Veronese, *ca.* 1468-1534). Painted in grisaille the panel was once the front of a cassone.

Draped over a lectern: *Chasuble* (Italian, XVc), a vestment of velvet and embroidery, with eight scenes from the life of Christ.

By the Court windows and around the room: set of thirteen *Chairs* with Hepplewhite-style shield backs and a matching backless sofa (Italian, late XVIIIc).

ANTONIAZZO ROMANO: THE ANNUNCIATION

On a marble column: Canosan *Vase* (South Italian, IIIc B.C.). A mask of Medusa is on the front, and three figures of Nike on the top, one shown driving her chariot.

To the left: marble *Bowl* with handles in the form of lions or panthers (Roman, imperial period).

Supporting the bowl: small *Altar with Dionysiac Reliefs* (Roman, probably II or IIIc).

Between the windows: *Cassone* (North Italian, late XVc) with three painted panels depicting historical or legendary incidents.

In the cassone: three *Chasubles* (Italian, XVI-XVIIIc), made of brocatelle and brocaded damask. Over the lid: velvet *Cope* (Spanish or Italian, dated 1670), with pomegranate design.

Above the cassone: two tempera paintings, each representing *A Hero of Antiquity* (Sienese, ca. 1500).

In the corner: *The Madonna and Child*, by Giovanni Bellini (Venetian, died 1516). Much damaged and restored, this is in Bellini's early style, *ca.* 1465.

Left, on the east wall: *The Tragedy of Lucretia*, by Sandro Botticelli (Florentine, 1444/5-1510). In the fashion of the times, several related episodes are united in a single picture with a formal architectural background remini-

SIENESE CASSONE

scent of a contemporary stage set. The story of the attack on the virtuous Lucretia by the son of the Tarquin king of Rome has been told by Livy, Ovid, and by Dante in his *Inferno,* and is traditionally the cause of the Roman ouster of the Tarquin kings and the establishment of the Republic in 509 B.C. The theme and the tenseness of the figures confirm this as a late work of the artist (after 1500) when the expulsion of the Medici and the presence of Savonarola had had their effect on Botticelli's style.

IN FRONT: wooden *Cassone* (Sienese, third quarter of the XVc). On the right are the arms of the Piccolomini, the family of Pope Pius II (who held the throne from 1458 to 1462), and on the left are the arms of the Todeschini, indicating that the chest had been made for a marriage between members of the two families.

IN THE CHEST: a rare 14-string *Guitar* (Italian, XVIIc), with bone inlay.

OVER THE DOORWAY: *The Virgin and Child, S. George and S. Martin,* by Francesc Comes (Spanish, active 1380-1395). The original frame is an example of Catalan and Aragonese Gothic woodcarving.

LEFT OF THE DOORWAY: *S. George and the Dragon,* by Carlo Crivelli (Venetian, active 1457-1495). This tempera painting on panel was once part of a large altarpiece painted in 1470 for the parish church at Porto S. Giorgio on the Adri-

CRIVELLI
S. GEORGE AND
THE DRAGON
(detail)

atic. To people of the ports along that sea, the saint's con-
quest of the dragon was a symbol of the destruction of
pirate ships.

ABOVE THE TABLE: *The Madonna and Child, with a Goldfinch,* attributed to Il Francia (Bolognese, *ca.* 1450-1517).

BEYOND: *Count Tommaso Inghirami,* portrait, oil on
panel by Raphael (Umbrian, 1483-1520). When Tommaso
Inghirami was two years old in 1472, his father, of a noble
family of Volterra, was killed in the sack of that city by
the Florentines. Lorenzo de' Medici took the child under
his protection at Florence and eleven years later sent him
to Rome. He rose in the Church, became a Canon of S.
Peter's and Papal Nuncio to the Emperor Maximilian. In
1510 Pope Julius II made him Chief Librarian of the
Vatican. Two years later he was appointed Secretary to the
Lateran Council and to the College of Cardinals The
portrait was probably painted in that year. Mrs. Gardner
purchased it from the Inghirami family in 1898. The version in the Pitti Palace at Florence is less impressive.

ON THE EASEL: *Pietà,* also by Raphael, painted probably
between 1503 and 1506, when the artist was about twenty

RAPHAEL
COUNT TOMMASO INGHIRAMI

and still strongly under the influence of Perugino. This influence shows in the figures, the feathery trees, and the vague distances. The painting was part of a large altarpiece done for the convent of S. Antonio at Perugia. It was bought by Mrs. Gardner in London, through Berenson, in 1900. The main panel and another predella panel are in the Metropolitan Museum, New York.

ABOVE THE WINDOW: one of a set of four Venetian *Mirrors* (XIXc), engraved with mythological figures.

ON THE PROJECTING WALL: majolica *Plate* (Umbrian, before 1550), representing the Nativity.

ON EITHER SIDE OF THE FIREPLACE: two large red velvet *Hangings* with the embroidered arms of Cardinal Hohenlohe (1823-1896), an important figure at the court of Pope Pius IX.

The *Apron of the Fireplace*, with its Latin inscription *MOTU ET LUMINE* (From motion, light) is North Italian, XVc.

ON THE WEST WALL, BY THE WINDOW: *The Madonna and Child with the Little S. John,* by Francesco Botticini (Florentine, 1446-1497), painted *ca.* 1480.

ABOVE THE LARGE VENETIAN COMMODE: *The Madonna and Child,* now catalogued as influenced by Andrea Mantegna. It has been variously attributed to Antonio della Corna, Bono da Ferrara and Bernardo Parentino, all North Italian painters of the XVc.

LEFT: *The Madonna and Child, with a Swallow,* by Pesellino. His style shows the influence of another Florentine painter, Filippo Lippi. The many versions and copies of this picture indicate its popularity in Florence.

THROUGH THE DOOR IN THE EAST WALL, THE SHORT GALLERY

BEHIND THE DOOR, ALONG THE WEST WALL: tall case containing a collection of Italian textiles, XV and XVIc.

ABOVE: portrait probably of *Mary Brough Stewart* (1744-1804), Mrs. Gardner's great-grandmother. The artist is unknown. Mrs. Stewart's fourth son, James (1778-1813), emigrated from Scotland to America and married Isabella Tod, whose portrait by Sully is in the corner to the right.

To the right, also at the top: *Isabella Stewart Gardner*, by Martin Mower (American, 1870-1960), painted in 1917 from a photograph of ten years earlier.
The brass bound inlaid *Folding Table* is Italian, late XVIIIc.

By the window: block-front Spanish mahogany *Chest-on-Chest*, of late XVIIIc New England origin, formerly owned by Mrs. Gardner's grandmother, Mrs. James Stewart.

Above the chest: portrait of *Isabella Tod Stewart*, by Thomas Sully (American, 1783-1872). She was the daughter of David Tod, who had come from England in 1761. Her youngest son, David, married Adelia Smith in 1839, and their daughter was Isabella Stewart Gardner.

On a stand: *A Gondolier*, drawing, ascribed to Vittore Carpaccio (Venetian, died *ca.* 1526). This is considered to be a study for a figure in Carpaccio's painting *The Miracle of the True Cross*, in the Accademia at Venice.

On the wall by the window: *The Flax Spinner*, fifth state of an etching by Jean François Millet (French, 1814-1875), made in 1868-1869. The unusual Italian frame is inlaid with marble and mother-of-pearl.

Right: carved teakwood Chinese *Cabinet*, containing a miscellany of small articles, mainly XIXc and two Turkish *Plates* (Iznik, late XVIIc).

Above: portrait of *John Lowell Gardner* (1837-1898), Mrs. Gardner's husband, painted at Venice in 1895 by Antonio

MANCINI
JOHN LOWELL GARDNER
(detail)

Mancini (Italian, 1852-1930). Mr. Gardner was a trustee and the treasurer of the Museum of Fine Arts, Boston, and was prominent in business and public undertakings.

To THE RIGHT, ON THE EAST WALL: *Mrs. Gardner in Venice,* by Anders Zorn, painted in the Palazzo Barbaro, Venice, in 1894. Fireworks over the Grand Canal can be seen in the background.

IN THE CABINET BELOW: a collection of Oriental articles and some family silver.

HIGH TO THE RIGHT: charcoal sketch of Mrs. Gardner's nephew *William Amory Gardner,* by William Morris Hunt (American, 1824-1879). He was long a master and a trustee at Groton School, and was among the signers of the papers of incorporation for the museum in 1900.

ABOVE RIGHT: *The Casa Loredan, Venice* (1850), drawing by the author and art critic John Ruskin (English, 1819-1900).

BELOW: *Secretary-bookcase* (English, late XVIIIc), containing many of Mrs. Gardner's books on the history of art.

BEYOND THE DOORWAY: four large *Cupboards* containing most of the prints and drawings in the collection. Designed by Mrs. Gardner, the doors open to panels with drawings that include Michelangelo's *Pietà* (Case I), *A*

MICHELANGELO
PIETÀ

BAKST
COSTUME FOR
ANNA PAVLOVA

Papal Procession by Raphael (Case I), and five by Matisse (Case I). There are thirty-seven prints by James McNeill Whistler (Case II) and eighty-two by Anders Zorn (Cases III and IV). Mounted on the outside of the FIRST DOOR, AT THE TOP, are two stipple engravings by Francesco Bartolozzi (Italian, 1725-1815): *Nymph of Immortality* and *Genius and Beauty.* BELOW: *Musicians with a Performing Dog,* red chalk on white paper, by Girolamo Romanino (Brescian, *ca.* 1485-1566); a small drawing in brown ink on white paper, *Christ and S. John the Baptist,* by Filippino Lippi (Italian, died 1504), son of Filippo Lippi, and in the same frame an engraving after it, in reverse, by Conrad Metz (German, 1749-1827), a pupil of Bartolozzi. LOWER LEFT: *Man in an Umbrian Costume,* lead point on white paper, Umbrian, late XVc. LOWER RIGHT: *A Man Pulling on a Loop,* lead point on white paper, workshop of Pietro Vanucci, called Perugino (Italian, 1446-1523).

ON THE SECOND DOOR are six prints by James McNeill Whistler. FROM THE TOP: *Old Battersea Bridge,* lithograph; *Waterloo Bridge,* lithograph (first state, 1896); *Old Battersea Bridge,* etching (1879 or earlier); *The Sisters,* lithograph (1894); *Conversation Under the Statue, Luxembourg Gardens,* lithograph (1893); *Study Number Two: A Young Girl Reading,* lithotint (1878).

On the third door, at the upper left: pencil and water-color sketch of a *Costume for Ida Rubinstein* in the ballet *Saint Sebastian*, by Léon Nikolaievitch Bakst (Russian, 1866-1924). At the upper right: *Costume for Anna Pavlova* in the *Oriental Ballet*, by the same artist. Both are characteristic of Bakst's celebrated designs for Diaghilev's Russian Ballet. Below: Five works by Degas: *Three Mounted Jockeys*, black ink and washes on brown paper; *La Sortie du Pesage*, pencil and watercolor on paper; *Cortège aux Environs de Florence*, pencil and wash on paper; two studies for the *Programme de la Soirée artistique*, black charcoal drawings (June 1884).

On the fourth door: a group of six etchings by Zorn. At the top: *A Toast, II* (fourth state, 1893) and *The Waltz* (third state, 1891); framed together: *Sunset or Bather (Evening) III* (second state, 1896), *Rosita Mauri* (second state, 1889), and *Mr. and Mrs. Fürstenberg* (second state, 1895). Below: *Mme George May, II* (first state, 1891) and *My Model and My Boat* (1894), inscribed: *an incomplete proof*. At the bottom: *The Little Brewery* (1890).

Right: *Flag*, First Regiment, Foot Grenadiers, Imperial Guard of Napoleon Bonaparte (1769-1821). Various em-blems of Napoleon — the cedar in a wreath, the eagle, bees, crowns, etc., are embroidered in gold. On the reverse are the names of all the battles in which the regiment participated.

On either side of the door: two French Empire *Cabinets* (early XIXc), with marble tops; the right-hand case con-tains mementos of Napoleon.

Along the west wall: four English *Side-Chairs* (late XVIIIc), Hepplewhite style. In the long glass case: vari-ous *Textiles*, all Italian of the XVI and XVIIc.

Above, right: *A Lady of the Russell Family (?)*, by Joseph Blackburn (American, active 1753-1763).

THROUGH THE DOOR IN THE EAST WALL, THE
LITTLE SALON

Much of the furniture and decorative woodwork in this room is a Venetian version of the French Louis XV style (XVIIIc). The more notable furnishings include the large *Mirror* between two *Windows* with decorated lower *Panels*: the smaller *Mirror* over the fireplace; the *Window Panelling* and *Molding* in the east wall; the gilded wood *Carving* above it; and the two concave *Doors,* in the northeast and southeast corners of the room, with the concave *Panels* beneath them.

The four *Tapestries* with scenes of courtly pleasures are called the *Château and Garden* series. Those on the south and west walls are from the Geubels family workshops in Brussels, late XVI and early XVIIc; while the two on the east wall were made in Paris at the shop of Raphael de la Planche, a Fleming, in the mid-XVIIc. The set belonged originally to Cardinal Antonio Barberini, nephew of Pope Urban VIII and Grand Prior of France.

TO THE LEFT OF THE FIREPLACE: *The Car of Venus,* by François Boucher (French, 1703-1770). The carved gilt frame is a good example of early Louis XV design. Having obtained the patronage of the Marquise de Pompadour, and

thus his future, Boucher spent his life turning out delicately voluptuous rococo Venuses and nymphs to decorate the palaces of the French nobility.

ON EITHER SIDE OF THE PAINTING: pair of Meissen *Sconces* (Dresden, XIXc), painted with fashionably dressed people in a landscape.

BELOW, ON THE TABLE: XVIIIc Meissen *Clock* and two *Candlesticks*. The clock movement is by Charles Baltazar (Paris, early XVIIIc).

ON THE MANTEL: late XVIII and early XIXc Meissen *Birds*; the bluejay on the far right is supposed to have come from the collection of Ludwig II of Bavaria.

IN THE NORTHEAST CORNER: three musical instruments. The single action pedal *Harp* was made by George Blaicher of Paris (active 1782-1828). The *Monochord* is mainly XIXc construction but made to look XVIIc. Its fixed bridge is raised by an apparatus controlled by the keyboard and marks an early stage in the development of the modern piano. The *Spinet* has been identified as English, school of Stephen Keene, London, *ca.* 1680.

IN THE SOUTHEAST CORNER: *Vitrine* (Italian, early XIXc) containing ancient coins, Chinese snuff bottles, and Japanese medicine cases or *inro*.

IN THE SOUTHWEST CORNER: *Vitrine* (Spanish, XVIIIc), gilt on gesso. TOP SHELF: four *Figure Groups* in creamware (French, XVIIIc); two more are on the middle shelf. Meissen *Mirror* and two *Birds* (Dresden, XVIIIc); small Sèvres *Cup and Saucer*, painted in 1756 by Taillandier and reputed to be from the collection of King Ludwig of Bavaria. SECOND SHELF: Wedgwood *Castor* in Queen's Ware (XVIIIc); octagonal miniature of *Marie-Antoinette* (*ca.* 1775). THIRD SHELF: Meissen figurine of a Shepherdess (mid-XIXc); white openwork creamware *Dish and Tray* (Leeds, *ca.* 1770); petit point and gros point embroidery of a *Lady with Flowers* (French or Flemish, XVIIc).

THROUGH THE DOOR IN THE SOUTH WALL, THE
TAPESTRY ROOM

This largest room in Fenway Court is the concert hall,
and concerts are given regularly except in July and August.
Originally it was the upper part of a two-story music
room. In 1914 Mrs. Gardner formed the Chinese Loggia,
Spanish Cloister, and East Cloister on the ground floor and
this Tapestry Room above. The ten large tapestries which
dominate the decoration of the room, and the great beams
in the ceiling, are mainly responsible for the fine acoustics.

These *Tapestries* were woven at Brussels in the mid-XVIc.
The set of five with a Latin inscription at the top depicts
scenes in the life of Abraham; the other set scenes in the
life of Cyrus the Great as described by Herodotus. In
accordance with artistic convention the settings and costumes in the Cyrus series are contemporary. The costumes
in the Abraham series reflect the artist's conception of

Old Testament dress. The arrangement of the tapestries around the walls is in conformity to the spaces available, not in chronological or subject sequence.

IN THE NORTHEAST CORNER: walnut *Credence* (Northern French *ca.* 1500). ON IT: *Ewer* of cast yellow bronze (Flemish, late XVc).
Two walnut *Chairs* (Italian, early XIXc), of a set of twelve in the room, in a revival of an earlier style.

ON THE WALL: brass *Plate,* with biblical motif, one of six in the room, all probably made in Nuremberg, XV-XVIIc.

ON AN EASEL AT THE WINDOW: *S. Engracia,* by Bartolomé Bermejo (Spanish, probably painted *ca.* 1474). The saint had been martyred in 304, under Diocletian. Her remains were discovered at Saragossa in the XIVc, and a church erected over the site. This is the central panel from the high altar of the church of S. Engracia, largely destroyed in 1806 during the siege of the city by the French.

ON THE OTHER SIDE OF THE EASEL: *Pope Innocent X* (1644-1655), a contemporary copy after the larger portrait painted in 1650 by Velázquez (Spanish, 1599-1660), now in the Doria-Pamfili Gallery, Rome.

ALONG THE WALL: *Lectern,* covered with red velvet bearing the arms of Pope Clement IX (1667-1669).
The iron *Pulpit* is perhaps Spanish or French (XIV-XVc).

UNDER THE PULPIT: walnut *Chest* (Spanish, XVIc).

BEYOND: tier of three oak *Choir Stalls* (French, XIV-XVc). The hinged seats have carved misericords which form a bracket rest when the seat is turned up, for the greater comfort of the person standing during long services.

The Gothic-arched stone *Window* to the right and the two *Windows* on either side of the fireplace on the south wall are all probably Spanish (late XIV or early XVc).

FLANKING THE FIREPLACE: two iron *Candelabra* (Flemish, late XVc). The French Gothic stone *Fireplace* dates from the reign of François I (1515-1547), though it has since been partly restored. In the center two angels support the symbol of the kings of France: a crowned shield with three fleur-de-lis. Animals and mythical beasts form a frieze along the sides.
The *Fireback* was a gift to Mrs. Gardner from Henry Mercer who made the floor tiles for the museum. It is a recast of one cast at the old Oxford Furnace in New Jersey in 1747.

OVER THE FIREPLACE: *S. Michael,* by Pedro García de Benabarre (Spanish, XVc). S. Michael is shown in his dual role, a warrior against Satan and a weigher of souls who hope to enter Paradise. This painting is one of the panels of a large altarpiece. Mrs. Gardner acquired it in 1916 through Professor Paul J. Sachs of Harvard.

AGAINST THE WEST WALL, RIGHT OF THE DOORWAY: black painted walnut *Chest* or *barqueño* (Spanish, XVIIc), a portable desk with small drawers behind a drop front. The F and Y are for Ferdinand and Isabella, commemorating the union of the East and West kingdoms. The stand is XIXc.

ABOVE THE CHEST: *La Gitana* (The Gypsy), by Louis Kronberg (painted at Seville in 1920).

OVERHEAD: large iron *Bracket with Lantern* (probably German, XVIIc).

ON THE STAND: Russian icon, *The Assumption of the Virgin* (probably school of Novgorod, XVc), with Christ enthroned in a mandorla above.

BELOW: *Silk Square*, painted by Isadora Duncan's brother Raymond (American, 1875-1966).

IN THE CENTER OF THE LONG TABLE: carved wood *Head of Christ* (South German, XVc), probably a fragment of a *Palmesel*. Such images of Christ seated on a donkey were drawn in processions on Palm Sunday.

IN FRONT OF THE WINDOWS: oak Jacobean *Dresser* (English, late XVIIc).

ON THE DRESSER, NEAR THE END: Persian *Manuscript of the Divan of Hafiz* (1489-1490). Five miniatures are inserted at irregular intervals into the text and illustrate this "Collection of Poems" by the celebrated poet Hafiz.

On a pedestal: polychromed wood candelabrum of the *Madonna della Misericordia* (Central Italian, XVIc), perhaps from Arezzo.

Beyond the windows: long oak *Refectory Table* (Spanish, XVIIc).

On the table: six *Miniatures* (Arabic and Persian, XIII-XVc), two from the *De Materia Medica* of Dioscurides (Baghdad, 1224), illustrating two medicinal plants; three from the *Automata* or *Book of Knowledge of Mechanical Devices* of al-Jazari (Egyptian, 1354); and two from the *Shah-nameh* or *Book of Kings* (Persian, XVc).

Right: upholstered *Sofa* (XIXc), with gros and petit point embroidery (English, early XVIIIc).

At the north end: oval *Table* (Italian, XVIIc), with the baluster legs characteristic of Bolognese work of that time.

In the center of the room, near the fireplace: oak *Draw Table* (Dutch, XVIIc). The extension leaves at each end are made to slide under the main top.

Above, supporting the ceiling beams: six wooden *Brackets* (Norman, XIVc or earlier), carved in grotesque forms of human beings and animals. The two full-length wooden ecclesiastical *Figures* may be English, XVIIc.

THROUGH THE DOORWAY IN THE WEST WALL, THE
SECOND FLOOR PASSAGE

Above the carved oak door: *The Vinegar Tasters*, two-fold screen (Japanese, XVIIc), depicting the famous legend when Confucius, Sakyamuni and Lao-tzu each took a taste of vinegar. Confucius called it sour, Sakyamuni bitter, and Lao-tzu sweet. It is implied that their teachings lead to the same truth, despite their different experiences.

To the right: *Chrysanthemums and Bamboo*, set of four sliding doors painted on gold ground (Kano school, Japanese, XVIIc). Three others of the set are on the opposite wall near the Court window.

BELOW: chain-stitch *Embroidery* (East Indian, XVIIc), probably made in Goa for the Portuguese trade.

OPPOSITE, ON THE WEST WALL, ABOVE: *Flowers and Birds*, six-fold screen on gold ground, also of the Kano school.

BELOW: *Young Pine Trees*, six-fold screen (Japanese, XVIIc), with a border-mounting made from strips of a XIVc Buddhist scriptural manuscript.

ON THE OPEN DOOR: large bronze *Knocker* of Neptune with two sea horses (copy after Alessandro Vittoria, Venetian, 1525-1608).

BELOW: panel of *Embroidery* with appliqué work (Italian, XVIc), taken from a chasuble.

THROUGH THE DOOR, THE
DUTCH ROOM

OVER THE DOORWAY: large needlepoint *Embroidery* (French, dating from the reign of Henry II, 1547-1559).

FLANKING THE DOORWAY: two portraits by Hans Holbein the Younger (German, 1497/8-1543) — *Sir William Butts, M.D.*, and *Lady Butts*, painted in the last year of Holbein's life. German by birth and having had an early period of employment at Basel, the painter worked largely in England after 1526 and became court painter to Henry VIII in 1536. William Butts, who died in 1545, was a scholar as well as court physician.

VAN DYCK
A LADY WITH A ROSE

BELOW: *Lady Butts,* stipple engraving, reproducing Holbein's drawing for this picture in Windsor Castle.

TO THE LEFT OF THE DOORWAY: one of a set of six Empire *Chairs* (French, XIXc), with figured damask.

IN THE CORNER: French walnut *Bread Cooler* or *panetière* (Arles, XVIIIc).

ON THE WALL: *A Lady in Black and White,* in the style of Bronzino (Florentine, 1503-1572), probably by one of his many XVIc imitators.

BETWEEN THE WINDOWS: high-backed *Bench,* walnut with inlay (Florentine, early XVIc), partly restored. Benches of this sort were often placed in patrician bedrooms.

ABOVE: *A Lady with a Rose,* by Antoon Van Dyck (Flemish, 1599-1641), court painter to Charles I of England, and briefly also to the Regent Isabella of Flanders, whose portrait by Pourbus is the last to the left on this wall. Van Dyck was a pupil and assistant of Rubens; after 1632 he settled in England and achieved eminence in his own right.

BEYOND: *A Man in a Fur Coat: 1521,* by Albrecht Dürer (German, 1471-1528). The picture has suffered losses, but the date and monogram survive. There are three suggested

REMBRANDT: SELF-PORTRAIT

VERMEER: THE CONCERT

identifications for the sitter: Lorenz Sterck, Lazarus Rav-
ensburger and Ruy Fernandes d'Almada.

LEFT: *Self-Portrait*, by Rembrandt Harmensz van Rijn
(Dutch, 1606-1669). The monogram *RHL* (to the right,
near the bottom) stands presumably for Rembrandt Har-
mensis-Leidensis and was used by him only until 1631/2,
while he was living in Leyden.

BELOW: the carved oak *Cabinet* is of XVIIc Dutch style,
but of XIXc manufacture. HANGING ON THE CABINET: etching, *Portrait of the Artist as a Young Man* (second state,
ca. 1633), by Rembrandt. The self-portrait has been
known since Bartsch's description as *Rembrandt aux trois
moustaches*.

ON EITHER SIDE OF THE CABINET: two *Chairs* (probably Italian) of a set of fourteen in the room, in the style of Louis
XIV.

OVER THE DOORWAY: painted wood statue in three-quarter
relief of *S. Martin and the Beggar* (Bavarian, *ca.* 1520).

LEFT: portrait of *Isabella Clara Eugenia, Archduchess of Austria* (1566-1633), by Frans Pourbus II (Flemish, 1569-1622). Isabella, daughter of Philip II of Spain, married an archduke of Austria and, with him, ruled the Catholic Netherlands for Spain. She patronized other Flemish painters, notably Rubens and Van Dyck. This painting was done soon after her marriage in 1598 and before 1600.

BELOW: ivory-inlay *Chest* (Venetian, XIXc), decorated in marquetry of burl walnut with satinwood borders.

IN THE CORNER (on a black wooden column with gilded capitals): one of four bronze *Candelabrum* (French, early XIXc).

ON AN EASEL, BY THE WINDOWS: *The Concert,* by Jan Vermeer (Dutch, 1632-1675), one of less than forty works that survive by the artist. Relatively unknown during his lifetime, he acquired posthumous fame in the XIXc as a master of domestic interiors revealed by daylight, here from an unseen window at the left. Mrs. Gardner bought the painting at the Thoré Burger sale in Paris, 1892.

ON THE OPPOSITE SIDE OF THE EASEL: *The Obelisk,* by Rembrandt, dated 1638. An obelisk like this once stood about two miles from Amsterdam, and is depicted in an etching by Rembrandt. The contour of the ground near Amsterdam, however, is different from that in the picture. The figures are almost overwhelmed by the sweeping composition of land, trees and sky.

ON THE TABLE IN FRONT: two rare Chinese tomb figurines — a serpentine *Pig* (Warring States period, *ca.* IIIc B.C.) and an earthenware *Dog* in an irridescent green glaze (Han dynasty, 206 B.C. — A.D. 220).

BESIDE THE FAR WINDOW: *The Virgin and Child,* an early XVIc copy, in reduced size, of a large painting in S. Martin's church at Colmar, Alsace, by Martin Schongauer (German, died 1491). The original is dated 1473.

ON TOP OF THE SILVER CABINET: *S. John the Baptist*, a bust in terracotta, workshop of Benedetto da Maiano (Florentine, 1442-1497).

TOP SHELF: silver gilt *Tankard*, made in Danzig, XVIIc; two silver *Goblets* (Paris, XVIIIc). SECOND SHELF: silver *Ostrich* mounted around an ostrich egg (German, XVIIc); small silver *Teapot* by Thos. Whipham and Chas. Wright (London, 1768-1769), on a *Tray* by J. McKay (Edinburgh, 1826-1827); two-handled *Cup* by R. Bayley (London, 1749). BOTTOM SHELF: silver *Tureen* and *Tray* made by Odiot (Paris, XIXc); silver *Candlestick* (London, 1648-1649); silver *Tankard* by Hans Pettersen Blytt (Bergen, ca. 1740); silver *Soap Box* by C. Eriksson (Swedish, 1858-1935) and made for Mrs. Gardner.

ALONG THE SOUTH WALL, RIGHT TO LEFT: *A Doctor of Law* at the University of Salamanca, by Francisco de Zurbarán (Spanish, 1598-1664). This portrait has been dated *ca.* 1658/60; the sitter is unknown.

BELOW: bronze *Beaker* or *Ku* (Chinese, Shang dynasty, 1200-1100 B.C.). The relief figures on the surface were produced by a delicate casting process. Represented in abstraction are the *t'ao-tieh* mask, a mythological monster, cloud spirals, and wind motifs.

LEFT: *The Storm on the Sea of Galilee,* by Rembrandt, with the date 1633 on the rudder. It is his only known

CHINESE KU

REMBRANDT
(detail)

RUBENS
EARL OF ARUNDEL

seascape. In his earlier years, scenes of violence appealed
to the painter and here he has chosen the moment when,
with the boat nearly overpowered by the sea, the disciples
wake Christ to tell him of their danger. The figure holding
onto his cap is a self-portrait of the artist.

ON THE SIDE OF THE LARGE OAK CABINET: *The Dauphin
François* (1517-1536), eldest son of François I of France
and heir to the throne. This is a contemporary copy of a
lost portrait by Corneille de Lyon (French, XVIc).

ABOVE: *The Madonna and Child*, by an unknown painter
under the influence of Rogier van der Weyden (Netherlandish, *ca.* 1400-1464).

TO THE LEFT: *Thomas Howard, Earl of Arundel* (1585-
1646), by Peter Paul Rubens (Flemish, 1577-1640), court
painter and diplomatic adviser to the Archduke Albert and
Archduchess Isabella (the latter represented in the Pourbus portrait in this room), and counselor and legate for
many rulers. His painting as well as his diplomatic service
was a feature in the courts of Europe. He was ennobled by
Philip IV of Spain and later received a Cambridge degree
and an English knighthood. While in England at one time,
1629, he visited Arundel. This painting may have been

made in that year or soon after. As portrayed, Thomas Howard wears the badge of a Knight of the Garter and carries the golden baton of the Earl Marshal or of the Lord High Constable of England. He had endured many difficulties with those in political ascendancy, and at one time was sent to the Tower. He retired from public life in 1641. He was an early collector of classical antiquities and a patron of the arts.

NEXT: *Anna van Bergen, Marquise of Veere* (1492-1541), after Jan Gossaert van Maubeuge, called Mabuse (Flemish, *ca.* 1478-1532).

BELOW: high-backed carved oak *Throne* (Auvergne, XVIc). The back and seat are modern restorations.

LEFT: *A Lady and Gentleman in Black,* by Rembrandt, painted in 1633 when he was twenty-seven, the year in which he painted *The Storm on the Sea of Galilee,* also in this room. He was then enjoying a period of success in Amsterdam and his work was much in demand.

The carved walnut *Cabinet* is Italian, late XVIc. ON THE CABINET: stoneware *Jug,* Grenzhausen ware (German, XVIIIc), bearing the arms of Amsterdam. The jug was found in excavating the cellar of the Old Brattle Street Church, Boston, and is supposed to have been brought to America by the Hessian or British soldiers who used the church as a barrack in 1775.

LEFT: *A Young Commander,* by Justus Suttermans (Flemish, 1597-1681). The sitter's costume dates the painting *ca.* 1650-1655. He may be a member of the Medici family since the artist was then their court painter.

ON THE EAST WALL: *A Lesson on the Theorbo,* by Gerard ter Borch (Dutch, 1617-1681). The artist's love of the subtle moment led him often to scenes of amateur music-making and these same characters repeat themselves in many of his paintings.

REMBRANDT: LADY AND GENTLEMAN IN BLACK

To the left: *Queen Mary of England*, from the studio of Anthonis Mor (Dutch, *ca.* 1519-1577). Mary (1516-1558), the only child to reach maturity of Henry VIII and his first wife, Catherine of Aragon, was England's first Queen Regnant. Her half-sister Elizabeth, born to Henry and Anne Boleyn, succeeded her as Queen Elizabeth I. This portrait, one of several versions of the original now in the Prado, was a preliminary of Mary's marriage with the future King Philip II of Spain. Mor was sent from Spain to paint it and the Queen received in exchange a portrait of Philip by Titian.

Below: upholstered walnut *Sofa* (French or Flemish, period of Louis Philippe, 1830-1848), with gros and petit

point embroidery dating from the late XVIIc and said to have been done by the nuns of the Abbey of Ronceray, at Angers.

RIGHT OF THE FIREPLACE: drawing, *The Annunciation*, a copy after a lost original by Rembrandt.

The red marble *Fireplace* is XVIc Italian. ON THE HOOD: marble inscribed *Panel* (Venetian, dated 1497).

ON THE MANTEL: two stone *Angels with Candlesticks*. The one on the left is Italian XVc and is close to the work of Domenico Rosselli (Florentine, *ca.* 1439-1497/8).

FLANKING THE FIREPLACE: two *Woodcarvings*, apparently cut down, representing the Nativity and the Resurrection (North Italian or South German, XVIc).

LEFT OF THE FIREPLACE: colored pencil sketch, *Three Captives* by Peter Paul Rubens, after Mantegna's *The Triumph of Caesar*.

BELOW: oak *Chest* with carved top (North German provincial, XVIIc).

ON THE CHEST: Dutch *Linen Press*, in the style of the XVIIc in Holland.

IN THE MIDDLE OF THE ROOM: large *Refectory Table* (Tuscan, with the date 1599 on the stretcher). The other table is also Italian, XVIc.

The *Painted Ceiling* is Italian, *ca.* 1500, with the arms of several Roman families. It may have come from a public building.

THROUGH THE DOORWAY IN THE NORTHWEST CORNER, THE SECOND FLOOR STAIR HALL, SOUTH

BEYOND THE FIRST COURT WINDOW: tapestry, *Man and Lady* (probably Flemish, XVIIIc). ABOVE: *The Battle of the River Uji* (Japanese, late XVIIc), eight-fold screen, depicting the famous race in 1182 between two rival warriors to determine who would be the first to cross the river and meet the enemy.

TO THE RIGHT OF THE WINDOW: tapestry (Flemish, late XVIc); the subject may be *Sinon Persuading Priam to Accept the Wooden Horse*.

The marble *Doorframe* is Venetian, *ca.* 1500, with the arms of Doge Andrea Gritti. ABOVE: tapestry, *Forest Scene* (Dutch or Flemish, late XVI or early XVIIc).

IN THE CORNER, LEFT TO RIGHT: two tapestries (Brussels, mid-XVIc), *Spring*, with the weaver's mark probably of Andreas Mattens, and *The Tower of Babel*, with the mark of Martin Reynbouts (1570-1619).

IN FRONT: octagonal *Table* (Florentine, XVIIIc), with pedestal legs in the form of sphinxes.

ON THE WALL OF THE STAIRWAY TO THE THIRD FLOOR: section of the *Lid (?) of a Sarcophagus* (Roman, *ca.* 300). BELOW: marble relief *Escutcheon* (Italian, XVIc), with wreath, of Andrea Valle, Bishop of Cotrone (1496-1508).

TO THE RIGHT, ON THE WALL OVER THE COURT WINDOWS: fresco fragment, *The Musicians*, perhaps Neapolitan, *ca.* 1610-1650.

III

THIRD FLOOR STAIR HALL, NORTH

ON THE WEST WALL, LEFT TO RIGHT: three Flemish tapestries. *Flemish Proverbs* (late XVc), a fragment of a larger tapestry illustrating nine folk proverbs against a *mille fleurs* background. *The Amazon Queens* (Franco-Flemish, ca. 1430), representing the preparation of the Amazons for their struggle with the Greeks. Seven richly dressed and jewelled women are seated on an arched balcony, the center one probably Orthia, the Amazon moon-goddess, and, in front of them, nine other women bearing armor for the two queens who stand at the right and left. *Esther Before Ahasuerus* (early XVIc), the scene depicted may be the fulfillment of Esther's promise to Mordecai: ". . . so will I go unto the king, which is not according to the law: and if I perish, I perish."

FLANKING THE DOORWAY: pair of gilded wood *Chancel Candlesticks* (Italian, XVI or XVIIc). OVER THE DOORWAY: iron *Bracket* (probably Sienese, XVI-XVIIc). TO THE RIGHT, ON THE EAST WALL: *A Lady in Black*, by Tintoretto (Venetian, 1518-1594). The black dress, perhaps of mourning, the severe ruff, and the cross of square-cut gems and hanging pearls suspended from the heavy necklace seem more Spanish than Venetian.

BELOW: walnut-veneered pine *Cupboard* (Italian, XVIIc). ON THE CUPBOARD: bronze *Bust of a Man* (Italian, XIXc).

RIGHT, BEYOND THE WINDOW: tapestry, *The Story of Jehu and Jezebel, and the Sons of Ahab* (Flemish, ca. 1470), from the story recounted in II Kings 9-10. Jehu, in a blue hat, appears in all five scenes. Typical of the work done at Tournai, the pattern is evenly distributed over the surface, free from blank areas and flatly conceived,

the artist frequently ignoring or distorting the effects of perspective.

BEYOND THE TRIPLE WINDOW: *Angel of the Annunciation* (Sienese, late XIVc), painted wood statue of the Archangel Gabriel. The companion piece, the *Annunciate Virgin*, is in the Musée Jacquemart-André, Paris.

DIVIDING THE HALLWAY: iron *Grill* and *Gate* (Italian, XVc).

TURNING BACK TO THE
VERONESE ROOM

The carved, gilded, and painted *Ceiling* in Early Renaissance style, made in Milan for the museum in 1901, provides a setting for *The Coronation of Hebe*, by an assistant of Veronese (Venetian, *ca.* 1528-1588). The central figure in this gathering of deities, Hebe was the daughter of Jupiter and Juno and the cupbearer of the gods. According to records this was painted for a ceiling in the della Torre palace at Udine, but the composition is designed for placement high on a vertical wall.

Covering the walls of the room are various pieces of tooled and gilded *Spanish Leather* that date from the XVII and XVIIIc.

TO THE RIGHT OF THE DOOR: walnut *Armchair* (Italian, early XVIIc), with tooled-leather back and seat, one of a set of six in the room.

ON THE WALL: large *Mirror* (Venetian, 1750-1800), engraved with figures of heroes of antiquity.

BELOW: *Commode* (Venetian, XVIIIc or later), in the Louis XVI style. ON THE COMMODE: *Toilet Mirror* (Venetian, Louis XV period, 1710-1774), and two majolica *Apothecary Jars* (XVIIIc).

BEYOND THE COURT WINDOW: *The Morning Toilet*, by Zorn, painted in 1888.

BELOW: *Armchair,* in the style of Louis XV (Venetian, mid-XVIIIc). Another stands in front of the table in the northeast corner.

To THE LEFT: painted *Tip-Table* (Italian, mid-XVIIIc). The oval top shows Diana seated in the clouds, with Apollo and Cupid.

AWAY FROM THE WALL: *Sedan Chair,* a composite of XVII-XIXc work, with painted garden scenes. Both the door inscription and the coat of arms on the back are spurious.

LEFT OF THE DOORWAY: *Sofa* (probably Venetian, XIXc) in the Louis XVI style.

ON THE WALL: *The Wedding of Barbarossa* by Giovanni Battista Tiepolo (Venetian, 1696-1770). The Holy Roman Emperor Frederick I, nicknamed Barbarossa (Red Beard), married Beatrice of Burgundy at Würzburg in 1156. This is a sketch for part of the fresco in the Kaisersaal of the Residenz of the Prince Bishop at Würzburg.

BELOW, RIGHT TO LEFT: four small pictures by Whistler: *The Sweet Shop, Chelsea* (oil on wood); *Lapis Lazuli* (pastel on cardboard); *The Violet Note* (pastel on cardboard); and *Mrs. Gardner in Yellow and Gold* (pastel on cardboard). The portrait sketch was done in London in 1886.

IN THE CORNER: *Writing Desk* (probably German, XIXc) of satinwood veneer, in the Adam style of the XVIIIc. The back of the desk is a pierced screen of scroll and lattice work with shaped and painted panels. *Gig Seat* (Venetian, XVIIIc), painted in *vernis Martin,* a reddish-brown varnish used in imitation of Chinese lacquer. The *pastiglia* decoration is in the *chinoiserie* style fashionable in Europe at the time.

ABOVE: *The Vision of S. Anthony of Padua,* oil on copper, by Filippo Lauri (North Italian, 1623-1694).

AWAY FROM THE WALL, ON THE TABLE: French Empire porcelain gilt *Tea Set.*

BETWEEN THE WINDOWS, NORTH WALL: marble-topped *Console Table* (Venetian, late XVIIIc). IN THE SMALL VITRINE: black glass *Madonna* (Murano, *ca.* 1600). "Black Madonnas" probably originated as reproductions of old and venerated Byzantine and Romanesque altar-figures which had become blackened by candlesmoke. The Venetian green glass *Candlesticks,* mounted in gilt bronze, are *ca.* 1700.

ON THE WALL ABOVE: *Alessandro Contarini* (?), by an anonymous Venetian. The inscription dates the portrait 1766 and identifies the subject as a Procurator of S. Mark's. The arms are those of the Contarini family, one of the oldest and best known in Venice.

IN THE VERTICAL CORNER CABINET: a variety of fine *Laces,* mainly of Italian origin.

No. 1 is a *Bed-Curtain* of Sicilian drawnwork, XVIc. The elaborate white work of that century was the result of an edict in the XVc forbidding the use of precious metals, jewels, and silk in the trimming of bedclothes.

No. 4 is also drawnwork of the XVIc, perhaps Sicilian. The linen is so fine and the stitches and outlines so crisp as to resemble mosaics.

No. 34 is made up of fourteen squares of Italian darned netting (XVII and XVIIIc), exact copies of designs by Federico Vinciolo published in 1543.

No. 75 is an early XVIIIc *Chalice Veil* of silk, with a mesh of needlepoint typical only of Burano.

No. 76, also from Burano with its square mesh, although a copy of French Alençon point lace. The clouded effect is the result of imperfectly spun thread, Italian spinning never having achieved the fineness and regularity of the Flemish.

ITALIAN
DARNED NETTING
NO. 34 (detail)

No. 91 is Binche bobbin lace (Flemish, early XVIIIc) demonstrating the typical Mechlin mesh of two threads twisted twice and four threads braided three times.

No. 93A is "point d'Angleterre" (Brussels, late XVIIc). It differs from the other Flemish bobbin laces, Mechlin and Binche, in that the pattern is woven first, and the bobbins are attached to the edge of the pattern to form the mesh. This piece is superlative by all three criteria for lace — design, technique, and fineness of thread.

BELOW, IN THE HORIZONTAL CORNER CASE:

No. 82, a Burano piece, is Venetian, late XVIIc, with well-defined figures. The technique is closely worked buttonhole stitch, with raised outlines used almost like shading.

No. 83 is XIXc Belgian mixed lace combining bobbin and needlepoint techniques.

No. 85, a flounce of needlepoint, is said to have been given by Louis XIV to the Spanish Cardinal.

No. 121 is XVIIc Spanish, a flounce of silver lace (silver leaf wound on silk thread), with appliquéd feather forms of the same thread.

No. 122, gold bobbin lace, is of the XIXc, probably Italian.

LEFT OF THE WINDOW, IN THE VERTICAL CASE:

No. 69, late XVIIc Venetian rosaline point flounce. The numerous small rosettes which ornament not only the pattern but also the picots are the reason for the name snowflake lace ("point de neige").

BELOW, IN THE HORIZONTAL CASE:

No. 72, a fragment of French needlepoint, is dated *ca.* 1675-1680 and is in the style of the artist Berain. This lace is part of a larger piece made during the reign of Louis XIV on the occasion of the marriage of the Dauphin, and is supposed to have belonged later to Marie-Antoinette. (Other fragments of the same original piece are now in the Brooklyn Museum and the Cleveland Museum of Art.)

No. 88 is a flounce of Mechlin lace (Flemish, late XVIIIc). Often called "the queen of laces" because of its filmy quality, Mechlin is made on the pillow in one process. By count it is said to have been ascertained that in this example the worker used 1,100 bobbins on her pillow at one time.

No. 89 is also Flemish bobbin lace, but of the XVIIc. The type is misnamed "point d'Angleterre" since it is neither point nor made in England. The misnomer stems from the time when the importation of foreign lace into England was prohibited, and this type of Flemish bobbin lace was smuggled in and sold as "English point."

TO THE RIGHT OF THE FIREPLACE: *Venice: The Clock Tower in the Piazza S. Marco* and *Venice Across the Basin of S. Marco,* both by Francesco Guardi (Venetian, 1712-1793). One of a family of painters, and a pupil of Canaletto, he is best known for his views of Venice and its canals. The faint colors of his skies and their reflections are the first steps in a new advance in the study of the atmosphere. In his later works, Guardi anticipated much of nineteenth century landscape painting.

GUARDI: VENICE ACROSS THE BASIN OF S. MARCO

IN FRONT: two Italian *Armchairs* (probably from Lombardy, mid-XVIIc).

TO THE LEFT, ABOVE: *The Story of David and Bathsheba*, by Herri met de Bles (Netherlandish, active 1535-1575). Three scenes from the Old Testament story are illustrated but they are overshadowed by the artist's interest in depicting all the fashionable outdoor pastimes of castle life in the XVIc — tennis, a jester, falconry, bathing, archery, a maze, and stag-hunting, with a highly fanciful landscape stretching into the far distance.

BELOW: *The Birth of Caterina Cornaro?* (1454-1510), by an unknown provincial artist (Venetian or Austrian, 1550-1600). Queen briefly of Jerusalem, Cyprus and Armenia, Caterina was a pawn in the political schemes of Venice throughout her life. Her story had become a favorite legend by the XVIc.

LEFT: carved and gilded *Lectern* (Italian, late XVIIIc). ON IT: ink and gouache drawing, *The Marriage of S. Catherine,* by Paolo Veronese. Despite variations in the composition this is probably a sketch for the painting done *ca.* 1575 by the artist for the church of S. Catherine at Venice.

IN THE CASE TO THE LEFT OF THE WINDOW: three *Fans* (French, XVIIIc).

THROUGH THE DOORWAY IN THE EAST WALL, TO THE
TITIAN ROOM

TO THE LEFT, ON THE WEST WALL: *The Child Jesus Disputing in the Temple,* by Paris Bordone (Venetian, 1500-1571), painted probably in the mid-1530's. The ambitious size and grandiose architecture are typical of the artist.

BELOW: English *Settee* (XVIII-XIXc), painted black with caned seat and back.

ON EITHER SIDE: pair of *Armchairs* (Italian, XVIIIc). There are two others of the set in this room.

RIGHT: *Juana of Austria, with (?) Her Niece Margaret,* by Alonso Sánchez Coello (Spanish, *ca.* 1531-1588). After Mor left the Spanish court in 1558, Sánchez became the favorite painter to Philip II. Juana (1535-1573) was the daughter of the Emperor Charles V and at eighteen was made Regent of Spain while her brother, Philip II, and father were in the Netherlands. She is represented in mourning for the death of her husband, the Infante of Portugal, who had died in 1554. The identification of the child is not certain.

RIGHT OF THE WINDOW: *The Continence of Scipio,* from the studio of Bonifazio Veronese (Venetian, 1487-1553). While on campaign in Spain in 209 B.C. the young Scipio Africanus restored to her family a captured Spanish maiden and the treasure offered as her ransom. A companion painting is on the opposite (south) wall of this room.

BELOW: red velvet *Hanging* (Italian, XVIc). ACROSS IT: *Halberd,* originally belonging to the household of Pope Paul V, 1605-1621 (Camillo Borghese, 1552-1621). The blade and handle are decorated with etched and inlaid designs, including phoenixes.

ON EITHER SIDE, ABOVE: two *Picture-Frames* (Italian, late XVc). The velvet brocade in the right-hand frame is Persian. BELOW: two small *Cabinets* (Italian, late XVIIIc) in the style of Louis XVI.

BETWEEN THE CABINETS: two high-backed *Side Chairs* (Venetian, XIXc), of English Jacobean style with marble inlay; and, two mahogany *Side Chairs* (Italian, early XIXc), of a set of six in the room.

BEYOND THE WINDOW, ON AN EASEL: *Christ Bearing the Cross,* oil on nut wood. A similar composition by Bellini is in Toledo, Ohio. This was bought as by Giorgione (died 1510) from the Palazzo Loschi in Vicenza and is often attributed to him. The names of Palma Vecchio and Andrea Previtali have also been proposed.

IN THE CABINET TO THE RIGHT: a collection of decanters, drinking glasses, vases, and glass boxes. Those etched with a coat of arms (castles and eagles) form a set

ATTRIBUTED TO
GIORGIONE
CHRIST BEARING
THE CROSS

(Dutch or Spanish, XVIIc). Another group of seventeen tumblers and five decanters are German, XVIIIc. Seven gilded wine glasses with a cardinal's arms are Saxon or Bavarian, XVIIIc. The two lavender *Cameo Vases* are by Emile Gallé (French, 1846-1904).

ON THE CABINET: marble *Bust of a Senator or Procurator* (Venetian, XVIIc), wearing an elaborate wig of long curls, and the velvet stole of office.

ON THE EAST WALL: *The Rape of Europa*, by Titian (Venetian, *ca.* 1477-1576). The picture was painted in Venice for Philip II of Spain in 1561/2, when Titian was eighty-five years old. On 26 April 1562 he wrote from Venice to his royal client:

> *Most Serene and Catholic King:*
>
> *With the help of Divine Providence I have at last finished the two pictures already begun for your Catholic Majesty. One is the "Christ praying in the*

Garden," the other the "Poesy of Europa carried by
the Bull," both of which I send, and I may say that
these put the seal on all that your Majesty was pleased
to order and I bound to deliver on various occasions.
                              Devoted humble servant
                                             Titian.

Royal inventories show the painting hung in the Alcáza,
Madrid and it influenced many artists. Velázquez trans-
lated it into the semblance of a tapestry placed in the
background of his work, *The Spinners*. Rubens in 1628/9
made a full-size copy of the *Europa* (now in the Prado,
Madrid), after which his pupil Van Dyck made the
sketch below. Much later, when the original painting
was in Paris, Watteau took suggestions from it in
developing his own picture on this subject.

The legend of Europa and the Bull is one of the
Greek myths repeated in Ovid's *Metamorphoses*. Zeus,
enamored of the Phoenician maiden Europa, changed
himself into a bull and appeared as a docile animal on a
shore where she was at play with other maidens. She
put flowers on his head and mounted to his back.
Slowly at first, so as not to frighten her, he walked into
the water, then swam off to Crete and revealed himself
to be king of the gods.

BELOW: two *Console Tables* (perhaps Roman, mid-
XVIIIc). ON THE LEFT-HAND TABLE: silver *Chalice* (Roman,
late XVIc), with the arms of the Colonna on the under-
side; bronze *Cupid*, attributed to François Duquesnoy
(Flemish, 1597-1643); enamelled copper *Plate* (Venetian,
XVIc). ON THE RIGHT-HAND TABLE: *The Rape of Europa*,
by Van Dyck (see under Titian), sketch in pencil and
water color; small bronze plaque, *The Rape of Europa*,
by Paul Manship (American, 1885-1966), given by the
artist to Mrs. Gardner at Christmas, 1917.

CELLINI: BINDO ALTOVITI

VELÁZQUEZ: KING PHILIP IV

OVER THE DOORWAY: *The Delivery of the Keys to S. Peter,* by Vincenzo Catena (Venetian, active 1500-1531). Another version of this is in the Prado, Madrid. The three blonde ladies who witness the delivery of the keys of heaven are Faith, Hope, and Charity.

RIGHT: *King Philip IV of Spain* (1605-1665), by Velázquez, a version of the portrait in Madrid. The inscription, lower left, stands for *Re Phelipe IV.* The eldest son of King Philip III and Margaret of Austria came to the throne in 1621 at the age of sixteen, and held it during more than forty years of turbulent rule. From his grandfather Philip II, he inherited both his great collection of pictures, including Titian's *Europa,* and his love of painting. His relations with Velázquez went beyond patron and court artist; he is said to have visited the studio daily, and Velázquez to have accompanied him whenever he left Madrid.

ON A COLUMN: *Bindo Altoviti* (1490-1556), dated 1550, one of two surviving portrait busts by Benvenuto Cellini (Florentine, 1500-1571). The sitter was a Florentine banker and patron of the arts. His portrait by Raphael is in the National Gallery, Washington, D. C. Cellini's autobiography includes a letter from Michelangelo praising this:

> *Dear Friend Benvenuto: I have for many years known you for one of the ablest jewelers in the world, and I now find that you have equal abilities as a sculptor. . . . Signor Bindo Altoviti showed me his bust in bronze, and told me that it was done by you. I was highly pleased with the execution, but it gave me great uneasiness to see it placed in a disadvantageous light; had it but been properly situated it would have appeared to have been the masterpiece it is.*

BEHIND: *Cope* (Italian, XVIc), with an ogival pattern and jardiniere and plant motifs.

RIGHT: *Self-Portrait* by Baccio Bandinelli (Florentine, 1488-1559), known mainly as a sculptor and a great rival of Cellini. He is shown wearing the badge of the Order of S. Iago, an honor he obtained in 1529.

BEYOND THE WINDOW: *A Girl with a Lute,* by Bartolommeo Veneto (active 1502-1546), painted presumably in Milan, where there are still three versions.

ABOVE: *The Magnanimity of Antigonus,* from the studio of Bonifazio Veronese. Antigonus, King of Macedonia (277-239 B.C.) gave up his young wife Stratonice to his son when the young man became ill from his concealed love for her.

BELOW: red velvet *Hanging* (Italian, XVIIIc), probably the drapery behind a prelate's throne. The embroidered badge is Dominican.

IN FRONT: fabric-covered *Chest* (Italian, XVIIIc) for storing laces and silks. The covering material is velvet brocade (probably Venetian, XVIIc), in the style of the early XVIc.

RIGHT: *The Nativity,* an early work by Liberale da Verona (Veronese, *ca.* 1445-1526).

BY THE DOUBLE WINDOW: six leather-covered walnut *Chairs* (Italian, XVIIIc).

IN THE CORNER: *A Bearded Man in Black,* painted in 1576 by Giovanni Battista Moroni (Brescian, *ca.* 1520-1578). He painted a number of large paintings for the churches of Bergamo where he lived and worked but his fame was based on his skill as a portrait painter.

RIGHT: *A Girl Taking a Thorn from her Foot,* derived from Raphael. The composition is taken from an early XVIc engraving which copied a fresco by Raphael in the Vatican palace.

BELOW: *Cope* (Italian or French, late XVIIc).

ON THE VENETIAN COMMODE: Japanese *hiramakié* (flat lacquer) *Chest,* with mother-of-pearl inlay and silver-dust ground. The chest, an example of Namban art, may have been made for a Dutch merchant mid-XVIIc.

ABOVE RIGHT, HIGH ON THE WALL: *A Lady in a Turban*, by Francesco Torbido (Veronese, *ca.* 1483-1561), a pupil of Liberale but in this portrait influenced by Titian.

BELOW: *Sacra Conversazione*, by Bonifazio Veronese, representing the Holy Family with S. John the Baptist and a female saint.

OVER THE DOOR: *Zacharias Vendramin*, a Procurator of S. Mark's, from the studio of Tintoretto. The Procurators exercised considerable power and were responsible for public building.

IN THE CENTER OF THE ROOM: Persian or Indian *Carpet* (XVIIc), of the so-called "Isfahan" type. Similar designs, originating in the Persian court ateliers, influenced textiles, stone carving, ceramics, and manuscript illumination.

ON THE CARPET: gilded *Armchairs* (Italian, XVIIIc) and two *Console Tables* (Italian, XIXc), with marble tops from Siena.

THROUGH THE DOORWAY IN THE EAST WALL, THE
LONG GALLERY

The Long Gallery divides itself into three sections, the first two separated, to the right of the entrance doorway, by the Moorish styled archway on double columns; the third section, farthest to the south, is the Chapel.

THE NORTHERN SECTION

LEFT OF THE DOORWAY: walnut *Armchair* (Spanish, XVI-XVIIc), one of four unmatched but similar chairs in the gallery.

ABOVE: glazed polychrome terracotta *Tabernacle Front*, from the workshop of Andrea della Robbia (Florentine, 1435-1525). The holy wafer was placed within the metal door.

ALONG THE WALL: large *Sideboard* (Florentine, late XVc), for storing church vestments. This is the finest piece of Italian furniture in the collection.

ON THE SIDEBOARD, LEFT TO RIGHT: marble bust of a *Young Man in a Dalmatic Vestment* (Roman? XVIc), most probably a portrait of Raphael Riario, Cardinal Sansoni (1460-1521), nephew of Sixtus IV. It may have been modeled on the bust in terracotta by Benedetto da Maiano in East Berlin. *Helmet* (North Indian, XVII or XVIIIc); *Fragment of a Mosque Lamp* (Syrian or Egyptian, mid-XIVc), brownish glass enamelled and gilt, the inscription around the rim is taken from the Koran; brass *Bowl* (Egyptian or Syrian, mid-XIVc or later), incised and inlaid with silver; marble relief *Bust of a Man* (North Italian, early XVIc), inscribed: PETRUS BON TREMOLUS.

ON THE WALL ABOVE: *The Madonna and Child of the Eucharist,* tempera on panel, by Botticelli, painted 1470. This picture is widely known as the Chigi Madonna, having hung until 1899 in the palace of the princes Chigi, now the Italian Foreign Office. An early work by

MINO DA FIESOLE

Botticelli, the design is unusually sculptural. His concentration on the symbolic separates him from Filippo Lippi, thought to have been his master. The Eucharist is represented by the ears of wheat and the bunches of grapes, which are to become the bread and wine.

NEAR THE WINDOW: marble relief *Bust of a Woman*, by Mino da Fiesole (Florentine, 1429-1484). The profile is like a relief in the Museo Nazionale, Florence, inscribed with the name of the artist.

BELOW: brass *Plate* (Venetian, XVIc), inlaid with silver and etched.

ON THE FLOOR: Japanese bronze *Basin* (mid-XIXc), for incense.

IN THE CORNER: *The Virgin Adoring the Child*, painted terracotta, attributed to Matteo Civitali (Luccan, 1436-1501).

RIGHT, ON THE WALL: tondo, *The Nativity*, probably from the studio of Botticelli, and the work of two hands, one of whom did the Virgin and the other Joseph. The latter shows the influence of Ghirlandaio.

BELOW: *Bench* (Italian, XVII-XVIIIc), gilt over gesso. One of a pair, the other is on the west side of the Chapel.

OPPOSITE THE DOORWAY: large *Canopy* and red velvet *Dossal* (Italian, XVIc), said to have been made for Francesco Cenci and woven with his initials and arms. He was a Prince of the Holy Roman Empire and father of the tragic Beatrice Cenci (1577-1599).

IN FRONT: marble relief of the *Madonna and Child,* by an imitator of Antonio Rossellino (Florentine, 1427-1478); possibly the work of Giovanni Bastianini (Italian, 1830-1868).

BENEATH: red *Cut-Velvet* on yellow satin ground (probably Venetian, XVIIc), following a Turkish design.

OVERHEAD, RIGHT: Spanish silver *Hanging Lamp*, with an inscription giving the date 1602 and naming the donors.

BELOW: *Prie-dieu* (North Italian, second half of the XVIIc), inlaid with satinwood, mahogany, and burl-walnut designs.

ON IT: *Processional Cross* (Spanish Gothic), silver-gilt and enamel, said to have come from Burgos Cathedral.

ABOVE: tondo relief in terracotta, *The Madonna and Child,* by Benedetto da Maiano (Florentine, 1442-1497). A late work similar to his Madonna in Sant'Agostino at San Gimignano. The frame is modern.

IN THE LONG CASE AGAINST THE WALL: *Letters* and *Autographs* of 13 American presidents: Washington, John Adams, Madison, Monroe, John Quincy Adams, Jackson, Tyler, Taylor, Fillmore, Grant, Cleveland, Theodore Roosevelt, and Taft. There are also *Letters* and *Autographs* of Franklin, John Randolph of Roanoke, Burr, Francis Scott Key, Daniel Webster, and Jefferson Davis.

ON A PEDESTAL TO THE RIGHT: white enameled terracotta *Bust of a Young Lady* (XIXc), in the style of Rossellino.

UCCELLO
A YOUNG LADY
OF FASHION

The four *Columns* supporting the Moorish style *Archway* are of *marmo di persica* (peach marble) and were purchased in Venice in 1899.

OPPOSITE: *A Young Lady of Fashion,* by Paolo Uccello (Florentine, *ca.* 1397-1475). This decorative type of profile was a standard form for portraiture in Florence during the first half of the XVc. Bought as the work of Domenico Veneziano, an attribution to the "Master of the Castello Nativity" is accepted by other scholars.

BELOW: small *Chest of Drawers,* of pine veneered in walnut and mahogany (from Bassano, near Venice, XVIIIc).

TO THE RIGHT: enameled terracotta relief, *The Lamentation,* by Giovanni della Robbia and assistants (Florentine, *ca.* 1469-1529). The inscription is from Lamentations 1:12 (Oh all ye that pass by, behold and see if there be any sorrow like unto my sorrow).

BELOW: strip of *Velvet Brocade* (Spanish or Italian, XVIc). Sargent used the design of this textile for the background in his portrait of Mrs. Gardner in the Gothic Room.

On either side: pair of iron *Torchères* (Venetian, XVIIIc).

On the cupboard to the right: marble *Torso* (Graeco-Roman, Julio-Claudian period).

On the farther side of the Moorish archway,

THE MIDDLE SECTION

In the case to the right: *Letters* and *Documents* bearing the autographs of Ferdinand V, Ferdinand and Isabella, Sir Francis Bacon, François I, Mazarin, Maria Theresa, the Marquise de Pompadour, Louis XVI, Marie-Antoinette, Bismarck, and others.

Above: marble *Herm Bust of a Greek Man of Affairs or Intellect* (Graeco-Roman, copy of a work of *ca.* 320-280 B.C.). The likeness is close to those of Epicurus and Metrodorus, leading philosophers of this period.

High on the wall: large painted wood *Escutcheon* (German, late XVIc), probably made for a castle banquet hall. The nine crests and twenty-one shields represent most of the reigning houses of what was to become modern Germany. It was given to Mrs. Gardner in 1902 by Sir Henry Irving.

Left: tall glass *Cabinet,* framed with gilt woodwork, containing Medieval and Early Renaissance religious articles.

On the top shelf: Limoges polychrome enamel *Pyx* and *Reliquary* (both XIVc); silver *Monstrance* (XVc), standing under a canopy is a tiny figure of a monastic saint, probably S. Dominic.

Second shelf: gilt *Processional Cross* (Spanish, XVc), on the arms are half-figures of the Virgin and S. John. The Corpus is in full relief. Bottom shelf: gilded *Chalice* (XVc); gilt copper *Monstrance* (German, XVIc), with small figures of SS. Bartholomew and James Major under the projecting canopies.

BEYOND THE WINDOW: small *Desk-Case*, containing *Memoriae* from XVc French Books of Hours, including *Miniatures* attributed to Jean Bourdichon (French, *ca.* 1457-1521), and thirty-seven *Miniatures* said to have been made for Anne de Bretagne (1477-1514).

ABOVE: gilt metal *Crucifix* (French, XIII-XIVc) and three framed *Illuminated Initials* from Antiphonals (North Italian, mid-XIVc), of SS. Martin, Laurence, and Michael.

ON THE WALL ABOVE: two green velvet *Copes* (Italian, XV-XVIc).

BELOW: painted carved wood *Frieze* (Burgundian, early XVIc), from a mantelpiece with two page boys holding a banner inscribed *De absentibus nil nisi bonum* (Of the absent nothing but good).

BETWEEN THE TWO DESK-CASES: two carved and inlaid *Armchairs* (North Italian, early XVIIIc).

LEFT, IN THE DESK-CASE: three Limoges polychrome enamel *Plaques. The Madonna and Child,* workshop of Jean I Limousin (*ca.* 1561-1610); *Pietà,* of an earlier date; and, *The Entombment,* from the workshop of Nardon Pénicaud (*ca.* 1470-1542), or Jean I Pénicaud (active *ca.* 1510-1540).

ABOVE: two small panel paintings, *SS. Jerome, Mary Magdalen and Francis,* from the studio of Paolo di Giovanni Fei; and, *The Martyrdom of S. Bartholomew,* by an unknown Florentine painter, *ca.* 1375-1425.

BY THE TRIPLE WINDOW, IN THE BOOKCASE: fine *Bindings* of rare editions of French and Italian literature, including those with the arms of Charles II, Cardinals Mazarin and Richelieu, Pope Gregory III, Henri's II, III, and IV, James II, Louis' XIII, XV, and XVI, and the Grand Dauphin, son of Louis XIV.

ON THE BOOKCASE: *Crowned Head* (Netherlandish or Burgundian, *ca.* 1400), polychromed stone. The faintly smiling face is a type which derives from Reims sculpture of the mid-XIIIc.

LEFT, IN THE WHISTLER AND SARGENT CASE: *Letters* and *Photographs* of Whistler, Sargent, and Denis Bunker; five sheets of pen and ink sketches for the *Peacock Room,* designed by Whistler for F. R. Leyland in 1876, now in the Freer Gallery, Washington.

BEYOND THE WINDOW: five *Choir Stalls* (North Italian, XVc). The back panels have intarsia work of the XVIc. The canopy support at one end has the carved figures of S. George and the dragon. Five more stalls from the original set are in the Gothic Room.

ABOVE: tapestry, *The Abduction* (perhaps Flemish, XVIIIc).

RETURNING TO THE MOORISH ARCH, ON THE (OUTER) WALL, IN THE CONTEMPORARY AUTHORS CASE: *Letters* and *Autographs,* including those of the Brownings, Carlyle, Dickens, Edward VII, Ibsen, George Eliot, Christina Rossetti, Ruskin, John Addington Symonds, Tennyson, Thackeray, and Wilde.

ON EITHER SIDE OF THE CASE: two carved and inlaid *Armchairs* (XVIIc, probably North Italian).

TO THE RIGHT, IN THE CASE OF MODERN PAINTERS AND SCULPTORS: *Letters* to Mrs. Gardner from Anisfeld, Cecilia Beaux, Ralph Curtis, Kronberg, La Farge, Macknight, Manship, Joseph Lindon Smith, and Zorn.

ABOVE: marble *Herm of Dionysos* (Graeco-Roman, *ca.* 50 B.C.-A.D. 125). The styling of hair and beard suggests that the face was reworked in Medieval times (probably North Italian, XIIIc).

ON THE WALL, LEFT TO RIGHT: *Battista, Countess of Urbino* (1446-1472), copy after the portrait by Piero della Francesca in the Uffizi, Florence. *The Madonna and Child,* after a composition attributed to Bernardino Luini

LONG GALLERY

(Milanese, *ca.* 1475-1532) in the Ambrosiana Gallery, Milan. *A Procurator of S. Mark's,* after a three-quarter length portrait by Tintoretto now in Berlin. This version may be a fragment of a larger picture. *The Adoration of the Kings,* by Joseph Lindon Smith (American, 1863-1950). A close friend of Mrs. Gardner's, he accompanied archaeological expeditions from Boston to Egypt and recorded their observations in paint, an example of which can be seen in the Blue Room.

RIGHT, IN THE CASE OF ENGLISH AUTHORS: *Autographs, Letters, Documents,* and *Manuscripts,* including letters of Burns, Schiller, Scott, Hood, and one from Pater to Mrs. Gardner; autographs of Ben Jonson, Charles II, Pepys, Thomas Campbell, and von Moltke; and manuscripts of Shelley's sonnet "To the Nile" and Keats' "Robin Hood."

RIGHT: marble *Cinerary Urn* (Roman, early imperial period), with sphinxes, rams' heads, cocks, volutes and

other forms. ON IT: marble *Bust of a Man* (Roman, style of *ca.* 150).

ON THE WALL: tapestry, *God Shows Noah the Rainbow as a Pledge* (Brussels, mid-XVIIc), with the mark of Jasper van Brugghen (active 1640-1655). This is the third in the series in the museum.

BELOW: walnut high-backed *Sacristy Bench* (Italian, in the style of the XVIIc). ON TOP OF THE BENCH, LEFT TO RIGHT: four small XVc reliefs, a *Standing Bishop on an Arcade* (Northern Spain), in alabaster; terracotta fragment of the *Madonna and Child* (Florentine); the *Man of Sorrows* (Perugian?), terracotta; and *S. Laurence* (probably Italian), in stone.

TO THE RIGHT: *Cinerarium* (Roman, I-IIc), with an inscribed plaque naming a Greek freedman. Garlands hanging from rams' heads flank the inscription. ON IT: marble *Head of a Youthful Divinity* (Graeco-Roman), after a work of *ca.* 465 B.C.

BY THE WINDOW, IN THE MARY, QUEEN OF SCOTS CASE: a fragment of green satin and one of Flemish mixed lace reputed to have belonged to Mary Stuart; her *Book of Hours*, printed at Paris in 1514 on vellum, with woodcuts and illuminated initials. The manuscript, *Form and Manner of Keeping the Parliament of England*, written for Edward VI, probably in 1547, the year of his accession. *Essays of Sir Francis Bacon*, printed at London in 1612, with the arms of James I stamped on both covers and with marginal notes in the king's own hand.

TO THE RIGHT, THE DANTE CASE: three early editions of the *Divine Comedy*, the Landino commentary of 1481 with nineteen engravings after designs by Botticelli; the Brescia copy of 1487, with sixty-eight woodcuts; and the Aldine edition of 1502, the first book to bear the printer's famous mark, an anchor around a dolphin. ALSO: a collection of eighteen Venetian *Manuscripts* (XVI-

CANTO SECONDO DELLA PRIMA CANTICA

XVIIIc) and *Letters* of Vittoria Colonna, Roberto Mala-testa, Federico, the Duke of Urbino, and Ludovico Maria Sforza, the Duke of Milan.

ON THE BOOKCASE: the *Virgin* and the *Angel Gabriel*, stone half-figures, by Giovanni Antonio Pilacorte (Venetian, *ca.* 1455-1531), from a choir rail.

ABOVE: *The Madonna and Child, with SS. Francis and Clare and Other Saints*, tempera transferred to modern panel, signed and dated 1307 by Giuliano da Rimini (active 1307-1346). The largest known altarpiece of the early Riminese school, it is also the earliest painting from that part of Italy. It shows the influence of Giotto and has served as a reference for dating certain of his frescoes.

GIULIANO DA RIMINI (detail)

Opposite, in the case of modern actors and French authors: (Left-hand section) *Letters* and *Photographs* to Mrs. Gardner from Sarah Bernhardt, Paul Bourget, Coquelin, Yvette Guilbert, Walter Hampden, Sir Henry Irving, and Ellen Terry. (Right-hand section) *Letters* of Voltaire, Rousseau, George Sand, Hugo, Jean François Millet, Edmond and Jules de Goncourt, Huysmans, Bergson, and Verlaine.

Above the case, left: *A Spanish Madonna,* oil sketch on wood by Sargent, inscribed to Mrs. Gardner.

On the wall, above: oval embroidered *Cartouche* (Italian, XVIc).

Above the case, right: painted terracotta tondo of the *Madonna and Child,* after Benedetto da Maiano.

THE CHAPEL

The most southerly third of the Long Gallery is a small mediaeval chapel in which, on Mrs. Gardner's birthday, the fourteenth of April, an Anglican High Mass is celebrated at her request by clergy of the Society of S. John the Evangelist.

Flanking the entrance: on staves set into stone impost blocks, two painted copper *Lanterns* (Venetian, XVII-XVIIIc), with quartz panes; and two low *Stalls* (French, XVc), with XVIc Italian red velvet cushions.

By the window, left: upholstered *Church Chair,* a XIXc Italian version in *lignum vitae* of a late XVIIIc French voyeuse, or spectator's chair, for sitting astride while resting the arms on the top. It was also used as a prie-dieu.

ABOVE THE WINDOW: painted wood *Madonna with a Bishop and King* (Franconian, mid-XVIIc).

OPPOSITE: walnut *Prie-Dieu* (Italian, XVIIc), with mother-of-pearl inlay. The *Chasuble* is satin on satin-velvet (Italian, XVI-XVIIc).

ABOVE: *The Wedding Feast at Cana,* by Tintoretto. One of his earliest paintings, it may be an exercise which the artist set himself.

LEFT: tall bronze *Candlestick* (Italian, XV-XVIc), one of four in the Chapel; range of two walnut *Choir Stalls* (Italian, XVI-XVIIc); gilt and painted wood *Standing Lantern* (Italian, probably XVc).

BEYOND THE DOORWAY, AND AROUND THE ALTAR: set of fifteen walnut *Choir Stalls* (Italian, XVIc), said to be from a monastery in the Veneto.

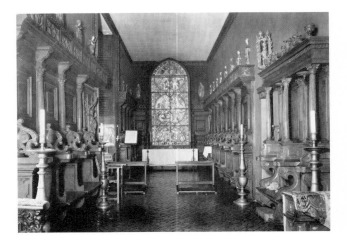

ON THE WALL, NEAREST THE ALCOVE: lindenwood statue of *S. Jerome* (German, Upper Rhine?, *ca.* 1500). The traceried tabernacle is modern.

IN THE ALCOVE, HIGH ON THE WALL: *The Interior of the Abbey Church of S. Denis*, by Paul-César Helleu (French, 1859-1927). Sargent, a friend of both the artist and Mrs. Gardner, recommended the picture.

BELOW: painted oak *Pietà* (Netherlandish, *ca.* 1500); pair of *Stained Glass Windows*, which with four windows in the Gothic Room are *ca.* 1500 from Milan Cathedral. They illustrate, left, Tobias taking leave of his parents and, right, the judgment of Solomon.

IN FRONT: large iron *Candelabrum* (probably Italian, XVc).

RIGHT, ON THE WALL: *The Annunciation*, by a South German provincial painter, *ca.* 1450-1500.

ON THE LECTERN: *Leaf from a Choir Book* (Italian, XVc), written for S. Laurence's Day.

OVER THE ALTAR: *Stained Glass Window* (Northern French, early XIIIc), much repaired through the centuries. Design and style are authentic; the pictorial subjects, however, may have been garbled during successive reconstructions. The prevailing theme of the original construction is assumed to have been scenes from the lives of SS. Nicaise and Eutropie.

The *Altar Frontal* is XVc Sicilian drawnwork.

BEHIND THE ALTAR, LEFT AND RIGHT: wood figures of *S. John* and a *Female Saint* (Ulm, *ca.* 1500).

ON THE WEST WALL, NEAR THE CORNER: *S. Philip Neri*, by an unknown Roman artist, *ca.* 1575-1595.

ON TOP OF THE STALLS, RIGHT: eight *Saints* (Bavarian, *ca.* 1510-1520), of polychromed wood, from an altar shrine. Those with attributes have been identified as Paul,

Stephen, Barbara, Agnes, and Dorothea. The other three may be Catherine, Peter and Laurence.

OVER THE DOORWAY: *S. Margaret* (Bavarian or Tyrolian, *ca.* 1520), carved in shallow relief for the wing of an altar.

THROUGH THE DOORWAY, THE
THIRD FLOOR PASSAGE

ON THE DOOR: small carved *Cupboard Door* (French, XIII-XIVc).

TO THE LEFT: *Listening to the Lute* (Japanese, Kano school, XVIIc), six-fold screen depicting Chinese gentlemen and their servants relaxing on a mountainside.

ON THE OPPOSITE WALL, ABOVE: *The Tale of Genji* (Japanese, XVIIc), pair of six-fold screens, showing various scenes from the popular and romantic novel about Prince Genji, written *ca.* 1000 A.D. by Lady Murasaki.

BELOW: *Pheasants and Small Birds* (Japanese, Kano school, late XVII-XVIIIc), six-fold screen.

IN FRONT: carved *Chest* (American, *ca.* 1675), with palm panels, oak sides, and a pine lid. RIGHT: walnut *Sacristy Bench* (Castilian, XVIIc).

HANGING ON THE ELEVATOR ENCLOSURE: four carved and gilded *Doors* (Chinese, late XIXc).

BY THE DOOR IN THE WEST WALL, THE
GOTHIC ROOM

The entrance doorway leads through a carved oak *Tambour* (Northern French, *ca.* 1500). This perhaps divided a spiral staircase from a room, or screened a doorway.

ABOVE THE TAMBOUR: *The Madonna and Child,* by an unknown Venetian painter, *ca.* 1425-1475. TO THE RIGHT:

round-arched panel painting, *The Madonna and Child with an Apple,* by an anonymous North Italian, *ca.* 1430-1480. An attribution to the "Master of Roncaiete" has been suggested.

HIGH UP ON THE WALLS: *Frieze* (North Italian, XVc), of sixty-eight paintings, portraits of illustrious people of the Renaissance. These are standard types with several panels repeated, some in different poses.

BELOW: walnut upholstered *Armchair* (Italian, XVIIc). The child's *Chair* in front of the tambour is early XVIIc Italian, as are the two children's *Chairs* in front of the fireplace. The *Day Bed* is late XVIIc English.

The *Fireplace* is Venetian, in the style of the XVc; the *Andirons,* with eccesiastical figures in relief, and the *Fireback* are French, XVc.

ABOVE THE FIREPLACE: *Altar of S. Maurice and the Theban Legion* (Upper Rhenish or Swiss, 1515), painted wood. S. Maurice, holding a red banner with a white cross, appears in the center of a group of thirteen warriors.

FLANKING THE FIREPLACE: two *Torchères* (French Gothic).

HANGING FROM THE CEILING: wrought iron *Lantern* (Italian, XVc).

ON THE FIREPLACE CANOPY: iron *Coat of Arms* of Queen Isabella of Spain (1451-1504), with an eagle mantling. The pomegranate was added to the arms of the Catholic kings after the taking of Granada in 1492.

TO THE RIGHT: walnut *Armchair* (Italian, XVIIc).

ON A WALL BRACKET: life-sized wood *Figure* (French, early XVIc), representing one of the Magi.

ALONG THE WALL: range of *Choir Stalls* (North Italian, XVc), five more of the set seen in the Long Gallery.

SOUTH GERMAN
MOUNTED FIGURE

ON TOP: *Mounted Figure* (South German, *ca.* 1470-1480), perhaps S. Hubert or S. Eustace. ABOVE: two-pointed embroidered *Banner* (Spanish, probably XVIIIc).

IN THE CORNER: gilt copper *Annunciation Angel* (Venetian, XVIIIc).

TO THE RIGHT: oak *Credence* (French, style of XVc). This is mainly of XIXc construction, but the linen-folds on the sides and the lock may be old. ON IT: painted terracotta *Bust of a Female Saint* (Italian, *ca.* 1500).

HIGH ON THE WALL: *S. Agnes* (Italian, XIVc, probably from Spoleto).

ON THE SOUTH WALL, CENTER: the stone *Wheel Window* may be Italian, XVc. It was not intended to hold glass, but to admit light and air.

AROUND IT: group of six *Stained Glass Windows*. The upper pair were made in Nuremberg, *ca.* 1490-1500. The donor, Lienhart Joechl, is shown with his family and patron saints Andrew and Peter. The four windows below are *ca.* 1500 from Milan Cathedral and illustrate, from left to right: Revelations 4:1-10, Christ washing the disciples' feet, and, possibly, the baptism of S. Eligius, the patron saint of metalworkers.

On the shelf, to the left: gilt and polychromed wood *Enthroned Virgin and Child* (Austrian or North Italian, *ca.* 1425), once part of an Adoration of the Magi.

In front: two *Armchairs* (North Italian, *ca.* 1600), of carved and inlaid walnut; wrought iron *Candelabra* (Spanish, XVIc), with the arms of the Bishop of Toledo.

Below the wheel window: carved walnut *Chest* (French, *ca.* 1525). On the chest: painted stucco *Madonna and Child* (Florentine, XVc), perhaps from the workshop of Ghiberti.

On the shelf, to the right: *Gabled Shrine with the Virgin and Child* (XVc, from the Veneto). The four gilt and painted *Angel Candlesticks* are Italian, XVIIc.

In front: three walnut *Chairs* (Italian, XVIIc), typical of the heavy furniture which completed baroque architectural interiors.

RIGHT: iron *Torchère* (Spanish, *ca.* 1400) and iron *Lectern* (probably French, XVc).
The oak *Credence* (French, *ca.* 1450) is largely restored.

ON THE CREDENCE: painted gilt stucco *Bust of a Woman* (Italian, XIXc).

HIGH ON THE WALL: *S. Agnes* (Aquila, *ca.* 1315).

IN THE SOUTHWEST CORNER: oak *Chest* (Spanish, XVc), with deeply-cut ogival tracery. The coat of arms of Rodrigo de Velasco, Bishop of Palencia (died 1485), is on the front.

ON THE CHEST: leather-bound *Choir Book* (Italian, mid-XVIIc). A late example of manuscript illumination, this is an *Antiphonarium* and contains music for the hourly prayers as well as the principal feast days. The colophon is signed by the copyist Brother Jerome.

BEHIND: portrait of *Isabella Stewart Gardner* (1888), by John Singer Sargent, when the artist was 32 and his subject 48. Mrs. Gardner has been quoted as saying that this was the ninth attempt, and she considered it the finest portrait Sargent ever painted. The friendship be-

SARGENT

ISABELLA
STEWART
GARDNER

(detail)

gun during the painting of this picture continued
throughout their lives. Mrs. Gardner is shown wearing
her famous pearls in three ropes, from each of which
hangs one of her three large rubies.

ON THE WALL: tapestry, *The Message to the Woodcutters*
(Franco-Flemish, early XVIc), probably woven at Tournai.

LIPPO MEMMI
MADONNA AND CHILD

BY THE GOTHIC-ARCHED WINDOWS, ON AN EASEL: *The
Madonna and Child,* by Lippo Memmi (Sienese, died
1357). This is a complete small altarpiece, well preserved.
The artist was the brother-in-law of Simone Martini,
who painted the large pentaptych in the Early Italian
Room. In the arcade are represented SS. Helen, Paul,
Domenic, Stephen, and a praying nun of some order
attached to the Dominicans, probably the donor of the
painting.

STANDING IN FRONT: *Peasant Chair* (provincial North
Italian, XVIIc). The carved back is removable from the
three-legged stool.

ON THE OPPOSITE SIDE OF THE EASEL: *The Presentation of the Infant Jesus in the Temple,* by Giotto di Bondone (Florentine, 1267-1336/7), depicting the story recounted in Luke 2. S. Joseph stands to the left holding the proper sacrifice of two young pigeons while the Child is returned to his mother by the priest Simeon. Anna, a prophetess of great age, observes from the right. Giotto's gift for narrative expressed through solid figures and simple gestures changed the course of European painting and prepared the ground for the painters of the next century. This is one of seven surviving panels from a series of scenes on the life of Christ.

IN FRONT: so-called *Dante Chair* (Italian, XVIc), a folding type common in the time of Dante and Giotto.

Beyond the windows: two *Ends of a Stall* (provincial French, *ca.* 1400), used here in the form of a bishop's throne and supporting a canopy. Above: lindenwood statue of *S. Elizabeth of Hungary* (Upper Rhenish or Swabian, *ca.* 1490).

In the corner: tapestry, *The Education of the Prince of Peace* (Tournai, early XVIc). The young prince stands in the foreground surrounded by allegorical figures, carefully labeled. The arms in the upper corners are of François de la Viefville and his wife Anne de Neufville.

Above the doorway: *S. Thomas Receives the Madonna's Girdle*, polyptych, by an unknown Ligurian *ca.* 1450-1500. The restored frame is an elaborate example of North Italian wood carving.

Across the top: carved *Beam* (French, probably XIVc).

Right: Spanish *Barqueño*, walnut, restored in the style of the XVIIc. On it: painted terracotta bust of *S. Bernardino of Siena*, 1380-1440 (Tuscan, XVc).

On the wall: *Adam and Eve,* ascribed to a follower of Lucas Cranach the Elder (German, 1472-1553). In the left background the expulsion from Paradise appears in miniature.

By the Court windows: four walnut *Armchairs* (probably Sicilian, XVIIc).

Between the windows, on the wall: carved *Triptych* of painted lindenwood (Saxon, *ca.* 1510-1520). The central panel is devoted to the Holy Kinship (*Die Helige Sippe*) and depicts S. Anne with her three husbands, three daughters, sons-in-law, and grandchildren. She and her daughter, the Virgin Mary, help support the Infant Christ. On the wings are four carved female saints, on the reverse are painted representations of four male saints.

BELOW: oak *Credence* (French, *ca.* 1500). An example of woodcarving from Lyon in which contemporary Italian motifs have been borrowed with freedom and grace.

HIGH ON THE WALL: *Madonna and Child* (Ile-de-France, mid-XIVc), limestone with modern polychromy; and fragments of a *Mille Fleurs Tapestry* (probably Flemish, early XVIc).

BY THE DOUBLE WINDOW: wrought iron *Reading Stand* (French, *ca.* 1300). Five silver *Plaques* (Italian, XIVc), perhaps from a crucifix; the figure of a bishop, Lazarus rising from the tomb (?), and the symbols of the Evangelists, SS. Mark, Luke, and John.

BEYOND THE WINDOWS, HIGH UP: *Altar of the Trinity with S. Catherine and a Bishop Saint* (North German, 1510-1520), attributed to the circle of Bernt Notke, the Lübeck master. The dating is based in part on the intricately carved foliage of the gable.

ON THE SIDEBOARD BELOW: pair of brass *Candlesticks* (Italian, XVIc) and a brass-bound leather-covered *Liqueur Chest* (Italian, XVIIc). The *Lace Cover* is Spanish darned netting, trimmed with a bobbin lace of Russian type.

**NORTH GERMAN
ALTAR OF THE TRINITY**

Out in the room, near the fireplace: walnut *Refectory Table* (Italian, XVIc). On the table is a chained book, *Sermons of Johann Nider,* printed by Conrad Fyner at Esslingen in 1476-1478. Both the binding and the chain are original. The *Chairs* around the table are Italian, *ca.* 1600.

Near the west end of the room: *Table* with a top of *cipollino rosso* marble (Venetian, XIXc). On the table: gilt metal *Processional Cross* (provincial Italian, XIV-XVc).

Between the tables: iron *Candlestand* (French, XIVc), called *couronne de fer* (iron crown).

Hanging from the ceiling: *Chandelier* (Bavarian, XVIc), made of two antlers and a painted wood kneeling figure.

Through the doorway, the
THIRD FLOOR STAIR HALL, SOUTH

Over the doorway: wood *Crucifix* (French or Spanish, XVIc).

Right: painted wood low relief figure of *S. Peter Martyr* (North Italian, late XVc).

On the west wall: painted terracotta relief of the *Entombment of Christ,* by Giovanni Minelli (Paduan, *ca.* 1460-1527). The kneeling figure at the left is Cerlota,

MINELLI
ENTOMBMENT OF CHRIST
(detail)

illegitimate daughter of James I, King of Cyprus. She died at the age of twelve, and this relief was made for the altar over her tomb, *ca.* 1483, in the church of Sant' Agostino, Padua. The frame is modern.

ON THE FLOOR, RIGHT: marble *Capital* (Venetian, XIIIc), with a XVc angel attached to one side.

AGAINST THE WALL: oak *Credence* (French, XVc), with a modern top.

ABOVE: pair of gilt and polychromed wood *Doors* (Spanish or French, XVc), probably from a church cupboard. Scenes from the life of the Virgin are carved in relief.

ACROSS, TO THE RIGHT OF THE COURT WINDOW: tapestry, *God Commands Noah to Build the Ark* (Brussels, mid-XVIIc).

BELOW: painted limestone *Retable* (French, early XVIc),
with a carved inscription and date of 1507. The coat of
arms is that of the Arnal family of Languedoc.

LEFT OF THE COURT WINDOW: wood figure of *Christ from
a Deposition Group* (Catalonian, XIIc). Such groups may
have been used during the Lenten and Easter liturgy to
illustrate scenes of the Passion.

INDEX OF THE ARTISTS MENTIONED

*The Roman numeral following the page number
indicates the museum floor.*

Angelico, Fra
The Dormition and Assumption of the Virgin 34   II
Antoniazzo Romano (attributed to)
The Annunciation   36   II

Bacchiacca   *A Lady with a Nosegay*   32   II
Bakst, Léon Nikolaievitch
Costume for Anna Pavlova   46   II
Costume for Ida Rubinstein   46   II
Baltazar, Charles   Clock movement   48   II
Bandinelli, Baccio   *Self-Portrait*   77   III
Bartolommeo Veneto   *A Girl with a Lute*   78   III
Bartolozzi, Francesco
Nymph of Immortality   45   II
Genius and Beauty   45   II
Bayley, Richard   Silver cup   58   II
Bellini, Gentile (attributed to) *A Turkish Artist* 32   II
Bellini, Giovanni   *The Madonna and Child*   38   II
Benedetto da Maiano   *The Madonna and Child* 82   III
Benedetto da Maiano (after)
A Young Man in a Dalmatic Vestment   80   III
The Madonna and Child   90   III
S. John the Baptist   58   II
Berain (style of)   Lace   70   III
Bermejo, Bartolomé   *S. Engracia*   50   II

Bicci di Lorenzo
  *The Madonna and Child, SS. Matthew
    and Francis*   34 II

Blackburn, Joseph
  A Lady of the Russell Family (?)   46 II

Blaicher, George   Harp   48 II

Blytt, Hans Pettersen   Silver tankard   58 II

Bonifazio Veronese   *Sacra Conversazione*   79 III

Bonifazio Veronese (studio of)
  The Continence of Scipio   72 III
  The Magnanimity of Antigonus   78 III

Borch, Gerard ter   *A Lesson on the Theorbo*   60 II

Bordone, Paris
  The Child Jesus Disputing in the Temple   72 III

Botticelli, Alessandro
  The Tragedy of Lucretia   38 II
  The Madonna and Child of the Eucharist 80 III

Botticelli (studio of)   *The Nativity*   81 III

Botticelli (engravings after)   *Divine Comedy* 88 III

Botticini, Francesco
  *The Madonna and Child with the
    Little S. John*   41 II

Boucher, François   *The Car of Venus*   47 II

Bourdichon, Jean   Miniatures   85 III

Bronzino, Angelo (style of)
  A Lady in Black and White   55 II

Brugghen, Jasper van
  Noah Builds the Ark, tapestry   29 II
  God Shows Noah the Rainbow as a Pledge,
    tapestry   88 III

Bulgarini, Bartolommeo
  *The Madonna Enthroned, with Saints
    and Angels*   34 II

Carpaccio, Vittore   *A Gondolier*   43   II
Catena, Vincenzo
   The Delivery of the Keys to S. Peter   76   III
Cellini, Benvenuto   *Bindo Altoviti*   77   III
Cicognara, Antonio   *A Prayer before a Tomb*   30   II
Cima da Conegliano (after)
   The Madonna and Child   37   II
Civitali, Matteo (attributed to)
   The Virgin Adoring the Child   81   III
Comes, Francesc
   *The Virgin and Child, S. George
   and S. Martin*   39   II
Corneille de Lyon (after)
   The Dauphin François   59   II
Corot, Jean Baptiste Camille   15   I
Courbet, Gustave   15   I
Cranach, Lucas (influenced by)   *Adam and Eve* 100   III
Credi, Lorenzo di   *A Boy in a Scarlet Cap*   32   II
Crivelli, Carlo   *S. George and the Dragon*   39   II

Daddi, Bernardo
   The Madonna and Child with a Goldfinch   35   II
Dante Alighieri
   Divine Comedy, Landino commentary, 1481   88   III
   Divine Comedy, Brescia edition, 1487   88   III
   Divine Comedy, Aldine edition, 1502   88   III
Degas, Hilaire Germain Edgar
   Mme Gaujelin   13   I
   La Sortie du Pesage   46   II
   Cortège aux Environs de Florence   46   II
   Three Mounted Jockeys   46   II
   Program, two drawings   46   II

Delacroix, Ferdinand Victor Eugène   15   I
Dioscurides (after)
      De Materia Medica, miniatures   53   II
Duncan, Raymond   Silk square   52   II
Duquesnoy, François   *Cupid*, bronze   75   III
Dürer, Albrecht   *A Man in a Fur Coat: 1521*   55   II
Dürer (after)
      S. Benedict Lying in the Briars, stained glass 16   I
Dyck, Antoon Van
      A Lady with a Rose   55   II
      The Rape of Europa   75   III

Eberle, Tomaso   Viola d'amore   14   I
Eriksson, Christian   Silver soap box   58   II

Falconetti, Giovanni Maria
      A Story from Antiquity   37   II
Fauré, Gabriel Urbain   Manuscript score   13   I
Fei, Paolo di Giovanni (attributed to)
      The Crucifixion, with Saints   34   II
Fei (studio of)
      SS. Jerome, Mary Magdalen and Francis   85   III
Francia, Francesco
      The Madonna and Child, with a Goldfinch   40   II

Gallé, Emile   Cameo vases   74   III
García, Pedro, de Benabarre   *S. Michael*   51   II
Gentile da Fabriano (style of)
      The Madonna of Humility, with a Donor   36   II
Gentile da Fabriano (influenced by)
      The Madonna and Child before a Rose Hedge   33   II

Gerini, Niccolò di Pietro
    S. Anthony Abbot, with Four Angels   33   II
Geubels, Jakob
    Château and Garden, tapestries   47   II
Ghiberti, Lorenzo (workshop of)
    The Madonna and Child   96   III
Giambono, Michele   *A Bishop Saint*   33   II
Giolfino, Bartolomeo (ascribed to)   Tabernacle 25   I
Giorgione (attributed to)
    Christ Bearing the Cross   73   III
Giotto di Bondone
    *The Presentation of the Infant Jesus
        in the Temple*   99   III
Giovanni di Paolo
    The Child Jesus Disputing in the Temple   35   II
Giovanni da Rovezzano (studio of)
    The Dormition of the Virgin, with a Nun   30   II
Giuliano da Rimini
    *The Madonna and Child, with SS. Francis
        and Clare and other Saints*   89   III
Gounod, Charles François   Manuscript score   13   I
Guardi, Francesco
    *Venice: The Clock Tower in the
        Piazza S. Marco*   70   III
    Venice across the Basin of S. Marco   70   III

Hafiz (after)   *The Divan,* manuscript   52   II
Helleu, Paul César
    *The Interior of the Abbey Church
        of S. Denis*   92   III
Herri met de Bles
    The Story of David and Bathsheba   71   III
Holbein, Hans
    Sir William Butts, M.D.   54   II
    Lady Butts   54   II
Hunt, William Morris   *William Amory Gardner*   44   II

James, William	*Henry James*	16	I
al-Jazari (after)	*Automata*, miniatures	53	II
Kano Yasukuni	Panel	28	I
Keats, John	*Robin Hood,* manuscript	87	III
Keene, Stephen (school of)	Spinet	48	II
Kronberg, Louis		24	I
La Gitana		51	II
Ladd, Anna Coleman	*Maria de Acosta Sargent*	25	I
La Farge, John		15	I
Lauri, Filippo			
The Vision of S. Anthony of Padua		67	III
Liberale da Verona	*The Nativity*	78	III
Limousin, Jean I (workshop of)			
The Madonna and Child, enamel		85	III
Lippi, Filippino	*Christ and S. John the Baptist*	45	II
Loeffler, Charles Martin	Manuscript score	13	I
Lorenzetti, Ambrogio	*S. Elizabeth of Hungary*	33	II
Luini, Bernardino (after)			
The Madonna and Child		86	III
Mabuse, Jan Gossaert van (after)			
Anna van Bergen, Marquise of Veere		60	II
Macknight, Dodge		24	I
Il Maestro Esiguo	*The Crucifixion*	33	II
Mancini, Antonio		15	I
John Lowell Gardner		43	II
Manet, Edouard			
Madame Auguste Manet		15	I
Chez Tortoni		15	I

Manship, Paul
  Diana, bronze   25   I
  The Rape of Europa, bronze plaque   75   III

Mantegna, Andrea   *Sacra Conversazione*   29   II

Mantegna (influenced by)
  The Madonna and Child   42   II

Masaccio
  A Young Man in a Scarlet Turban   30   II

Matisse, Henri   45   II
  The Terrace, St. Tropez   14   I

Mattens, Andreas   *Spring*, tapestry   63   II

McKay, J.   Silver tray   58   II

Memmi, Lippo   *The Madonna and Child*   98   III

Mercer, Henry   Tile floors   29   II

Metz, Conrad Martin
  Christ and S. John the Baptist   45   II

Michelangelo   *Pietà*   44   II

Millet, Jean François   *The Flax Spinner*   43   II

Minelli, Giovanni   *The Entombment of Christ*   102   III

Mino da Fiesole   *A Bust of a Woman*   81   III

Mor, Anthonis (studio of)
  Queen Mary of England   61   II

Moroni, Giovanni Battista
  A Bearded Man in Black   78   III

Mosca, Giovanni Maria
  Madonna della Ruota della Carità   28   I

Mower, Martin   24   I
  Isabella Stewart Gardner   43   II

Notke, Bernt (influenced by)
  *The Altar of the Trinity with S. Catherine
  and a Bishop Saint*   101 III

Odiot, Charles   Silver tureen and tray   58   II

Pasti, Matteo de'
  Isotta degli Atti, medal   35   II
Pénicaud, Jean I or Nardon (workshop of)
  The Entombment, enamel   85 III
Pesellino, Francesco
  The Triumphs of Love, Chastity and Death   31   II
  The Triumphs of Fame, Time and Eternity   31   II
  The Madonna and Child, with a Swallow   42   II
Piero della Francesca   *Hercules*   31   II
Piero della Francesca (after)
  Battista, Countess of Urbino   86 III
Pilacorte, Giovanni Antonio
  The Virgin and *Angel Gabriel*   89 III
Pintoricchio   *The Madonna and Child*   35   II
Pisanello
  Sigismondo Pandolfo Malatesta, medal   35   II
  Niccolò Piccinino, medal   35   II
  Filippo Maria Visconti, medal   35   II
Planche, Raphael de la
  Château and Garden, tapestries   47   II
Pollaiuolo, Piero del
  A Woman in Green and Crimson   36   II
Pope, Arthur   24   I
Pourbus, Frans II
  *Isabella Clara Eugenia, Archduchess
  of Austria*   56   II
Praxiteles (after)   Dionysos torso   19   I
Praxiteles (style of)   *Head of Apollo (?)*   24   I

Raphael
    Count Tommaso Inghirami   40 II
    Pietà   40 II
    A Papal Procession   45 II

Raphael (derived from)
    A Girl Taking a Thorn from her Foot   78 III

Rembrandt Harmensz van Rijn
    Self-Portrait   56 II
    The Obelisk   57 II
    The Storm on the Sea of Galilee   58 II
    A Lady and Gentleman in Black   60 II
    Portrait of the Artist as a Young Man, etching 56 II

Rembrandt (after)   *The Annunciation*   62 II

Reynbouts, Martin
    The Tower of Babel, tapestry   63 II

Robbia, Andrea della (workshop of)
    Tabernacle front   79 III

Robbia, Giovanni della
    The Lamentation   83 III

Romanino, Girolamo
    Musicians with a Performing Dog   45 II

Ronceray Abbey   Embroidery   62 II

Ross, Denman Waldo   24 I

Rosselli, Domenico (after)
    An Angel with a Candlestick   62 II

Rossellino, Antonio (style of)
    A Bust of a Young Lady   82 III

Rossellino (imitator of)
    The Madonna and Child   82 III

Rossetti, Dante Gabriel   *Love's Greeting*   13 I

Rubens, Peter Paul
    Thomas Howard, Earl of Arundel   59 II
    Three Captives   62 II

Rubinstein, Anton   Manuscript score   13 I

Ruskin, John   *The Casa Loredan, Venice*   44 II

Sánchez Coello, Alonso
   Juana of Austria, with (?) her niece Margaret 72 III

Sargent, John Singer   15   I
   Charles Martin Loeffler   13   I
   El Jaleo   17   I
   A Spanish Madonna   90 III
   Isabella Stewart Gardner   97 III
   Mrs. Gardner in White   25   I
   Rio di San Salvatore   25   I
   S. Maria dei Gesuati   25   I
   Thomas Whittemore   25   I

Schongauer, Martin (after)
   The Virgin and Child   57 II

Shelley, Percy Bysshe *To the Nile*, manuscript 87 III

Simone Martini
   The Madonna and Child, with Four Saints 32 II

Smith, Joseph Lindon
   The Adoration of the Kings   87 III

Sully, Thomas *Isabella Tod Stewart*   43 II

Suttermans, Justus *A Young Commander*   60 II

Taillandier Sèvres cup and saucer   48 II

Tchaikovsky, Peter Ilich
   Manuscript score, fragment   13   I

Tiepolo, Giovanni Battista
   The Wedding of Barbarossa   67 III

Tintoretto, Jacopo
   A Lady in Black   64 III
   The Wedding Feast at Cana   91 III

Tintoretto (studio of) *Zacharias Vendramin* 79 III

Tintoretto (after)
   A Procurator of S. Mark's   87 III

Titian *The Rape of Europa*   74 III

Torbido, Francesco *A Lady in a Turban* 79 III

Tura, Cosimo   *The Circumcision*   30   II
Turner, Joseph Mallord William
   The Roman Tower, Andernach   14   I
Twachtman, John Henry   24   I

Uccello, Paolo   *A Young Lady of Fashion*   83 III

Velázquez, Diego   *King Philip IV of Spain*   76 III
Velázquez (after)   *Pope Innocent X*   50   II
Vermeer, Johannes   *The Concert*   57   II
Veronese, Paolo   *The Marriage of S. Catherine*   71 III
Veronese (by an assistant of)
   The Coronation of Hebe   65 III
Vinciolo, Federico (after)   Lace   68 III
Vittoria, Alessandro (after)   Bronze knocker   54   II

Weyden, Rogier van der (influenced by)
   The Madonna and Child   59   II
Whipham, Thomas, and Wright, Charles
   Silver teapot   58   II
Whistler, James Abbott McNeill
   Nocturne, Blue and Silver: Battersea Reach   13   I
   Harmony in Blue and Silver: Trouville   13   I
   The Sweet Shop, Chelsea   67 III
   Lapis Lazuli   67 III
   The Violet Note   67 III
   Mrs. Gardner in Yellow and Gold   67 III
   Peacock Room, sketches   86 III
   Old Battersea Bridge   45   II
   Waterloo Bridge   45   II
   The Sisters   45   II
   *Conversation under the Statue, Luxembourg
      Gardens*   45   II
   Study of a Young Lady Reading   45   II

Yvernel   *Sèvres plates*   15   I

Zorn, Anders Leonard   15   I
    Mrs. Gardner in Venice   44   II
    The Morning Toilet   66   III
    Mme Georges May, II   46   II
    My Model and My Boat   46   II
    A Toast, II   46   II
    The Waltz   46   II
    Sunset or Bather (Evening) III   46   II
    Rosita Mauri   46   II
    Mr. and Mrs. Fürstenberg   46   II
    The Little Brewery   46   II
Zurbarán, Francisco de   *A Doctor of Law*   58   II
Zurbarán (studio of)   *The Virgin of Mercy*   17   I

NOTES